2020
The Get Up and Go Dia

ISBN 978-1-9109

Published in Ireland by
GET UP AND GO PUBLICATIONS LTD
Camboline, Hazelwood, Sligo, F91 NP04, Ireland.
Email: info@getupandgodiary.com
www.getupandgodiary.com

Compiled by Eileen Forrestal
Graphic design by Nuala Redmond
Illustrations: Sophia Murray; dreamstime.com; shutterstock.com
Printed in Ireland by GPS Colour Graphics.

2020 BANK AND PUBLIC HOLIDAYS

REPUBLIC OF IRELAND

New Year's Day, 1 January;
St Patrick's Day, 17 March;
Good Friday, 10 April;
Easter Monday, 13 April;
May Day Bank Holiday, 4 May;
June Bank Holiday, 1 June;
August Bank Holiday, 3 August;
October Bank Holiday, 26 October;
Christmas Day, 25 December;
St Stephen's Day, 26 December.

NORTHERN IRELAND

New Year's Day, 1 January;
Good Friday, 10 April;
May Day Holiday, 4 May;
Orangemen's Holiday, 13 July;
Christmas Day, 25 December;
St Patrick's Day, 17 March;
Easter Monday, 13 April;
Spring Bank Holiday, 25 May;
Summer Bank Holiday, 31 August;
Boxing Day, 26 December.

ENGLAND, SCOTLAND AND WALES

New Year's Day, 1 January;
Easter Monday, 13 April;
May Day Holiday, 4 May;
Summer Bank Holiday, 31 August;
Christmas Day, 25 December;
Good Friday, 10 April;
St George's Day, 23 April
Spring Bank Holiday, 25 May;
Remembrance Sunday, 8 November;
Boxing Day, 26 December.

UNITED STATES OF AMERICA

New Year's Day, 1 January;
Presidents' Day, 17 February;
Independence Day, 4 July;
Columbus Day, 12 October;
Thanksgiving Day, 26 November;
Martin Luther King Day, 20 January;
Memorial Day, 25 May;
Labour Day, 7 September;
Veterans Day, 11 November;
Christmas Day, 25 December.

CANADA

New Year's Day, 1 January;
Heritage Day, 17 February;
St Patrick's Day, 17 March;
Easter Monday, 13 April;
Canada Day, 1 July;
Thanksgiving Day, 12 October;
Christmas Day, 25 December;
Family Day, 17 February;
Commonwealth Day, 9 March;
Good Friday, 10 April;
Victoria Day 18 May;
Labour Day, 7 September;
Rememberance Day, 11 November;
Boxing Day, 26 December.

AUSTRALIA (NATIONAL HOLIDAYS)

New Year's Day, 1 January;
Good Friday, 10 April;
Anzac Day 25 April;
Christmas Day, 25 December;
Australia Day, 27 January;
Easter Monday, 13 April;
Queen's Birthday, 8 June;
Boxing Day, 26 December.

2020 CALENDAR

January

S	M	T	W	T	F	S
			1	2	3	4
5	6	7	8	9	10	11
12	13	14	15	16	17	18
19	20	21	22	23	24	25
26	27	28	29	30	31	

February

S	M	T	W	T	F	S
						1
2	3	4	5	6	7	8
9	10	11	12	13	14	15
16	17	18	19	20	21	22
23	24	25	26	27	28	29

March

S	M	T	W	T	F	S
1	2	3	4	5	6	7
8	9	10	11	12	13	14
15	16	17	18	19	20	21
22	23	24	25	26	27	28
29	30	31				

April

S	M	T	W	T	F	S
			1	2	3	4
5	6	7	8	9	10	11
12	13	14	15	16	17	18
19	20	21	22	23	24	25
26	27	28	29	30		

May

S	M	T	W	T	F	S
					1	2
3	4	5	6	7	8	9
10	11	12	13	14	15	16
17	18	19	20	21	22	23
24	25	26	27	28	29	30
31						

June

S	M	T	W	T	F	S
	1	2	3	4	5	6
7	8	9	10	11	12	13
14	15	16	17	18	19	20
21	22	23	24	25	26	27
28	29	30				

July

S	M	T	W	T	F	S
			1	2	3	4
5	6	7	8	9	10	11
12	13	14	15	16	17	18
19	20	21	22	23	24	25
26	27	28	29	30	31	

August

S	M	T	W	T	F	S
						1
2	3	4	5	6	7	8
9	10	11	12	13	14	15
16	17	18	19	20	21	22
23	24	25	26	27	28	29
30	31					

September

S	M	T	W	T	F	S
		1	2	3	4	5
6	7	8	9	10	11	12
13	14	15	16	17	18	19
20	21	22	23	24	25	26
27	28	29	30			

October

S	M	T	W	T	F	S
				1	2	3
4	5	6	7	8	9	10
11	12	13	14	15	16	17
18	19	20	21	22	23	24
25	26	27	28	29	30	31

November

S	M	T	W	T	F	S
1	2	3	4	5	6	7
8	9	10	11	12	13	14
15	16	17	18	19	20	21
22	23	24	25	26	27	28
29	30					

December

S	M	T	W	T	F	S
		1	2	3	4	5
6	7	8	9	10	11	12
13	14	15	16	17	18	19
20	21	22	23	24	25	26
27	28	29	30	31		

Forgive the past – let it go
Live the present – the power of now
Create the future – thoughts become things

Dear Reader,

We are delighted that you're holding this Get Up and Go diary in your hands today. You are about to embark on a wonderful journey with 'the world's best loved transformational diary'.

Whether this is your first Get Up and Go diary or you're a regular and loyal customer, we thank you, and we trust that you will benefit from the carefully chosen words contained herein.

You may have chosen this diary for yourself or received it as gift from a friend; either way, we know it will fill your days with inspiration, encouragement, motivation and empowerment in the year ahead.

You may also like to follow us on Facebook, Twitter and Instagram for additional timely words of inspiration and encouragement. Please check out our website **www.getupandgodiary.com** where you can find out about (and purchase) new products, follow our blog, learn about upcoming events and see details of special offers.

Also there's something extra we think you'll appreciate. Through our partnership with the Global Giving Initiative www.B1G1.com this diary is changing lives – a contribution from each Get Up and Go diary goes towards providing children in rural Cambodia with access to clean water, children in rural India enjoying e-learning and we're helping to build a school in Kenya. You'll see more about all of that on our webite.

And it all happens because people like you love their Get Up and Go diary. Thank you so much for being one of them.

With very best wishes for the year ahead,

Brendan Sands

Eileen Forrestal

This diary belongs to: ______________________________

Address: ______________________________

Tel: ____________________ Email: ____________________

Emergency telephone number: ____________________

BUCKET LIST for January

The new year stands before us, like a chapter in a book, waiting to be written. We can help write that story by setting goals.

Melody Beattie

Life's not about sitting at home in front of the TV waiting for your life to begin. Get out there and take some chances.

Queen Latifah

And now we welcome the New Year. Full of things that have never been.

Rainer Maria Rilke

January

New Year new Start

For last year's words
belong to last year's language
and next year's words await
another voice.

TS Eliot

Forgive yourself for what you think you've done or not done. At every moment, you had your reasons for all of your actions and decisions. You've always done the best that you could do. Forgive yourself.

Doreen Virtue

No matter who you are, no matter what you did, no matter where you've come from, you can always change, become a better version of yourself.

Madonna

WEDNESDAY **1**

Let your smile shine

NEW YEAR'S RESOLUTIONS FOR PEACE OF MIND

12 things to give up … seriously'

Give up complaining.
Give up criticising.
Give up making excuses.
Give up brooding on the past.
Give up regrets.
Give up resentments.
Give up expectations.
Give up making yourself, or other people, wrong.
Give up comparing yourself to others.
Give up the need to control everything.
Give up your resistance to change.
Give up your need to impress others.

THURSDAY **2**

Your time is precious – manage it

FRIDAY **3**

Enjoy your free time

January

The root of the word courage is *cor* – the Latin word for heart. In one of its earliest forms, the word courage had a very different definition than it does today. Courage originally meant: "To speak one's mind by telling all one's heart". Over time, this definition has changed, and today, courage is more synonymous with being heroic. Heroics is important and we certainly need heroes, but I think we've lost touch with the idea that speaking honestly and openly about who we are, about what we're feeling, and about our experiences (good and bad) is the definition of courage. Heroics is often about putting our life on the line. Ordinary courage is about putting our vulnerability on the line. In today's world that's pretty extraordinary.

Brené Brown

SATURDAY **4**

Welcome silence into your life

SUNDAY **5**

Lighten up

What the new year brings to you will depend a great deal on what you bring to the new year.

Vern McLellan

I hope that in this year to come, you make mistakes. Because if you are making mistakes, then you are making new things, trying new things, learning, living, pushing yourself, changing yourself, changing your world. You're doing things you've never done before, and more importantly, you're doing something.

Neil Gaiman

Wine is constant proof that God loves us and loves to see us happy.

Nothing will work unless you do.

Maya Angelou

You were born with potential.
You were born with goodness and trust.
You were born with ideals and dreams.
You were born with greatness.
You were born with wings.
You are not meant for crawling, so don't.
You have wings. Learn to use them and fly.

Rumi

Baked potato filled with spinach

GLUTEN AND DAIRY FREE – FROM MAMA RAE

WHAT YOU WILL NEED

1 Sweet potato for each person
3 cups spinach
1 ½ tablespoons oil
2 cloves crushed garlic
Salt and pepper
1/3 cup walnuts
3 tablespoons cranberries

THE HOW-TO PART

Cook sweet potatoes in oven on 180 degrees for 45 minutes or until done. Saute the garlic in the oil for 3 minutes, add the spinach and cook until just wilted. Add salt and pepper. Cut the top off the potato and fill with the spinach mix. Sprinkle with the chopped walnuts and cranberries.

SECRETS FROM MAMA RAE'S KITCHEN

Add 3 chopped spring onions. You can serve this with some nut cheese (¾ cup cashews,1/2 cup of water, 3 teaspoons nutritional yeast, ½ teaspoon salt. Process all ingredients together. You may need to use a little more water to make it thicker.)

You never know how strong you are until being strong is your only choice.

With the new day comes new strength and new thoughts.

Eleanor Roosevelt

MONDAY **6**

Write your action plan

TUESDAY **7**

You are exactly where you are meant to be

People are always blaming circumstances for what they are. I do not believe in circumstances. The people who get on in this world are the people who get up and look for the circumstances they want, and if they cannot find them, make them.

George Bernard Shaw

Change your life today. Don't gamble on the future, act now, without delay.

Simone de Beauvoir

Stop wearing your wishbone where your backbone ought to be.

Elizabeth Gilbert

WEDNESDAY **8**

Congratulate yourself on your accomplishments to date

THURSDAY **9**

Slow down and breathe

FRIDAY **10**

Let go of fixed ideas about how things 'should' be

SATURDAY **11**

Look at it all from a wider perspective

SUNDAY **12**

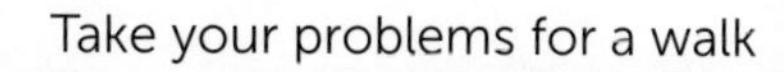

Take your problems for a walk

January

The future belongs to those who believe in the beauty of their dreams.

Eleanor Roosevelt

MONDAY **13**

Accept compliments graciously

TUESDAY **14**

Stay away from persistent complainers

I've got to take chances and get out there. What are you going to do, sit home and knit? I don't knit.

Cybill Shepherd

WEDNESDAY **15**

If you need to say something, say it

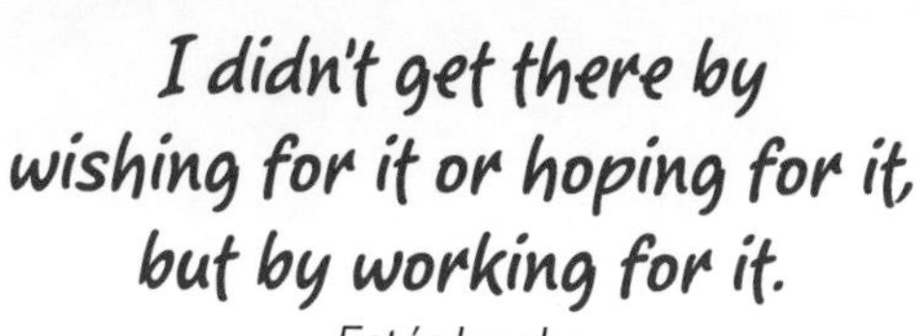

Estée Lauder

The most difficult thing is the decision to act. The rest is merely tenacity.

Amelia Earhart

THURSDAY **16**

Do what you need to do to get out of debt

FRIDAY **17**

Schedule your relaxation time.

SATURDAY **18**

Plan a date with yourself

SUNDAY **19**

Be your own best friend

January

BIG JOURNEYS BEGIN WITH SMALL STEPS

It is imperative that a woman keep her sense of humour intact and at the ready. She must see, even if only in secret, that she is the funniest, looniest woman in her world, which she should also see as being the most absurd world of all times. It has been said that laughter is therapeutic and amiability lengthens the life span. Women should be tough, tender, laugh as much as possible, and live long lives. The struggle for balance and equality continues unabated, and the woman warrior who is armed with wit and courage will be among the first to celebrate victory.

Maya Angelou

MONDAY **20**

Take time to wonder

TUESDAY **21**

Write down everything you love about your life

Remember always that you not only have the right to be an individual, you have an obligation to be one.

Eleanor Roosevelt

WEDNESDAY **22**

Ignore your inner critic

THURSDAY **23**

Listen with an open heart

FRIDAY **24**

Hold your loved ones close

SATURDAY **25**

Stay cool, calm and collected

SUNDAY **26**

Don't undermine your worth by comparing yourself to others

MONDAY **27**

You are here to enrich the world

TUESDAY **28**

Listen to your favourite music

WEDNESDAY **29**

Life is not about watching from the side-lines –get involved!

THURSDAY **30**

Make the most of what you've got

FRIDAY **31**

Don't dwell on past events; they happened and they're over now

Your task is not to seek for love, but merely to seek and find all the barriers within yourself that you have built against it.

BUCKET LIST

Let yourself be silently drawn by the stronger pull of what you really love.

TIPS TO BEING WELL

Pay attention to your overall health and happiness.
It's important.
Maintain control of your thoughts and feelings – they're fickle!
Be resilient in the face of challenges.
Find ways to express your creativity.
Understand the importance of social connections.
Recognise the power of spirituality.
Discover the value of staying positive.
Make time for yourself.
Nurture your friendships.
Don't feel guilty about pleasure.
Indulge yourself with random pamper days.
Don't ignore feelings of stress hoping they will go away.
Be kind to yourself – do nice things for you.
When your mind is frazzled take a step back, take a deep breath and take a good look around you. It grounds you.
Practice daily meditation to inspire peace and relaxation.
Being happy goes a long way to nurture your being well.

Let no one remove my
wrinkles from my forehead,
obtained through wonder
before the beauty of life;
or those of my mouth, which show how
much I laughed and how much I kissed;
and not the bags under my eyes: In them
are the memories of how much I cried.
They are mine and they are beautiful.

Meryl Streep

if YOU NEVER try} YOU'LL NEVER know

Spend time with those you love. One of these days you will say either, "I wish I had," or "I'm glad I did."

Zig Ziglar

As we work to create light for others, we naturally light our own way.

Mary Anne Radmacher

There cannot be a crisis next week. My schedule is already full.

Henry A Kissinger

SATURDAY **1**

Love life and it will love you back

SUNDAY **2**

Asking saves a lot of guesswork

21 WAYS TO KEEP YOUR RELATIONSHIP

STRONG

Make your relationship a priority.
Accept that disappointments will happen.
Practice forgiveness.
Be generous with admiration and compliments.
Engage in meaningful conversation.
Let go of the desire to fix or change your partner.
Accept responsibility for how you show up in your relationship.
Focus on the qualities you love and respect in your partner.
Trust that your partner has good intentions.
Learn how to be fully present.
Bring your best to the relationship.
Make it clear that you want to hear and understand your partner.
Be open and share what is important to you.
Ask your partner to share what is important to them.
In a dispute, give the relationship a vote.
Learn what needs to happen for your partner to feel loved and respected.
Understand we all have baggage – best to leave it behind.
Respect each others' boundaries.
Respect yourself and express your thoughts and feelings openly.
Beware of keeping secrets 'to protect' your partner!
Own your own limiting beliefs.
Be true to your word.
Take the time to express appreciation.
Daydream together.

Believe in yourself

**Love is friendship that has caught fire.
It is quiet understanding, mutual confidence, sharing and forgiving. It is loyalty through good and bad times. It settles for less than perfection and makes allowances for human weaknesses.**

Ann Landers

MONDAY **3**

Keep an open mind for what's possible

TUESDAY **4**

Face life's challenges with courage

WEDNESDAY **5**

A little work, a little play, keeps us going, every day

**Healthy mind + healthy body = TOTAL HEALTH.
Take the time to nurture both.**

THURSDAY **6**

Life is an emotional journey

FRIDAY **7**

Be the person you hoped you would become

SATURDAY **8**

Dare yourself to love more

Remind yourself: "I've come a long way".

After all is said and done, sit down.

Bill Copeland

SUNDAY **9**

Create what you are looking for

Anyone who says he can see through women is missing a lot.

Groucho Marx

MONDAY **10**

Give peace a chance

TUESDAY **11**

Avoid electronic overload

WEDNESDAY **12**

If you enjoy your life, your children will enjoy theirs

THURSDAY **13**

Every downside has an upside

Treat your senses. Do little things that make you happy and stimulate your senses, like lighting a scented candle, buying some fresh-cut flowers, indulging in a massage or treating yourself to your favourite food or drink.

FRIDAY **14**
St Valentine's Day

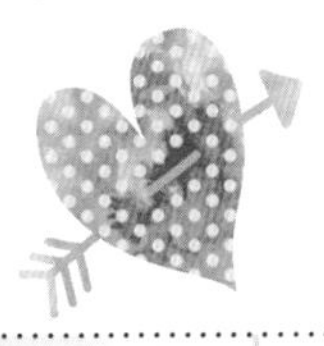

Let what you love inspire your life

SATURDAY **15**

It doesn't hurt to be gracious

SUNDAY **16**

Honesty pays

Light is to darkness what love is to fear; in the presence of one, the other disappears.

Marianne Williamson

Running a multimillion dollar business can feel like a piece of cake when facing a defiant and dramatic teenage daughter.

Colleen O'Grady

Taking joy in living is woman's best cosmetic.

Rosalind Russell

MONDAY **17**

A thankful heart is a great virtue

TUESDAY **18**

Live your life as a conscious role model

WEDNESDAY **19**

Don't fail to plan and plan to succeed

THURSDAY **20**

Become a 'possibilitiarian'

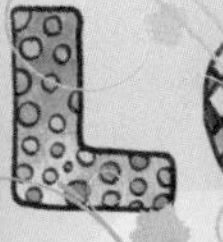
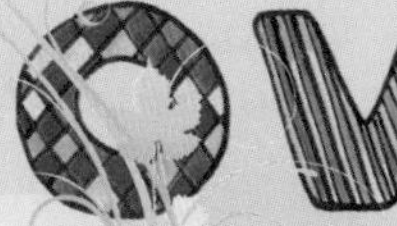

I have yet to hear a man ask for advice on how to combine marriage and a career.

Gloria Steinem

Sleep. Everyone gets cranky without enough sleep, so dedicate adequate sleep time every night. And treat yourself to a nap every now and then.

FRIDAY **21**

A lie can never fix the truth

SATURDAY **22**

Telling the truth is a courageous act

SUNDAY **23**

Start a new beginning today

Buckwheat pancakes

GLUTEN, DAIRY, AND REFINED SUGAR FREE – FROM MAMA RAE

WHAT YOU WILL NEED

½ cup buckwheat flour
½ teaspoon baking soda
Pinch of salt
½ cup almond milk
1 teaspoon apple cider vinegar

THE HOW-TO PART

Sift the flour salt and baking powder.
Add the apple cider vinegar to the milk. Gently fold in the milk until the milk is absorbed. Stand in the refrigerator for 15-30 minutes. Heat a non-stick fry-pan and pour batter in. Cook pancakes until bubbles appear on the top and then flip. Drizzle with honey or serve with fresh fruit or berries.

SECRETS FROM MAMA RAE'S KITCHEN

Use the milk you normally use. You can add ½ teaspoon cumin and serve with tomatoes, mushrooms and spinach. Add a teaspoon of maple syrup/honey and serve with stewed/ fresh fruit in season. If you are in a hurry you can leave out the chill 15-30 minutes. These are great served as an accompaniment to a curry dish.

February

*Make time for laziness.
You don't have to be constantly
on the go.*

MONDAY **24**

There are at least two sides to every story

TUESDAY **25**

Everyone is beautiful with a smile

WEDNESDAY **26**

Never forget a kindness

THURSDAY **27**

Remember those who encouraged you

FRIDAY **28**

Take the advice you give to others

SATURDAY **29**

Be the best friend you ever have

BLOGGING TIPS

(can also apply to video)

Just do it – don't sweat it.
Shorter is better.
Make your headline intriguing.
Use sub headings above some paragraphs.
Get to the point fast.
Keep your paragraphs short.
Write in the first person.
Choose your audience and write for them.
Write as you would speak to a valued friend.
A picture speaks a 1000 words.
No acronyms, no jargon.
Write about what you are passionate about.
Don't try to be perfect.
Your writing is the vehicle –
your message is what's important.
Proof read before posting.
Check spelling, grammar and punctuation.
Be inviting, be engaging, ask questions.
Be yourself.

Feeling Good

Everybody, everywhere seeks happiness, it's true,
But finding it, and keeping it, seem difficult to do.
Difficult because we think that happiness is found
Only in the places where wealth and fame abound.
And so we go on searching in palaces of pleasure
Seeking recognition and monetary treasure,
Unaware that happiness is just a state of mind
Within the reach of everyone who takes time to be kind.
For in making others happy, we will be happy, too,
and the happiness you give away returns to shine on you.

Helen Steiner Rice

SUNDAY **1**

A home is made of love and dreams

March

The difference between successful people and others is how much time they spend feeling sorry for themselves.

It takes one woman twenty years to make a man of her son and another woman twenty minutes to make a fool of him.

Helen Rowland

MONDAY **2**

What you do now will be evident later

Failing is not a crime. What is important is if you fail, you have the energy and the will to pull yourself up and keep going.

Wangari Maathai

TUESDAY **3**

Trust is essential for good relations

HELP YOURSELF TO HAPPINESS

May you have enough happiness to make you sweet, enough trials to make you strong, enough sorrow to keep you human and enough hope to make you happy.

The happiest of people don't necessarily have the best of everything; they just make the most of everything that comes along their way. The brightest future will always be based on a forgotten past; you can't go forward in life until you let go of your past failures and heartaches.

When you were born, you were crying and everyone around you was smiling. Live your life, so at the end, you're the one who is smiling and everyone around you is crying.

Share your precious moments with people who value you; those who have touched your life in some way; those who make you smile when you really need it; those who make you see the brighter side of things when you are feeling down; those whose care and friendship you truly appreciate; those who give your life meaning; those who let you be who you are.

Don't count the years, count the memories.

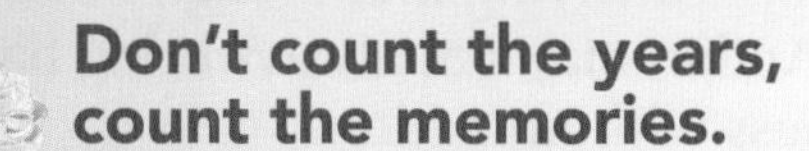

The message that underlies healing is simple, yet radical: We are already whole.

Underneath our fears and worries, unaffected by the many layers of our conditioning and actions, is a peaceful core.

The work of healing is peeling away the barriers of fear that keep us unaware of our true nature, of love, peace and rich inter-connection with the web of life.

Healing is the rediscovery of who we are, and who we have always been.

Joan Borysenko

MORE THOUGHTS ON HAPPINESS

There is no way to happiness. Happiness is the way.
Be true to your higher self. Being a good human being, and the way to true inner happiness, is through altruistic actions, being mindful of others, doing no harm.
You are good enough just as you are.
Breathe and relax in the happiness of this thought.
Happiness is a function of accepting what is, and letting go of what is not.
People are usually as happy as they make up their minds to be.
Very little is needed to be happy in life; it is all within yourself, in your attitude and your way of thinking. Happiness is when what you think, what you say and what you do are in harmony.
Happiness comes through doors you didn't even know were open.
Make space for happiness in your day. Clear out the clutter that's in the way, including pessimistic thinking and pessimistic thinkers.
Life is short; make fun of it. The sooner you can laugh at yourself, the sooner you will be living life, truly.
Live for something that is bigger than you are.
It will lead to a happier, more satisfying life, though not necessarily an easier one. Action may not always bring happiness, but there is no true happiness without action.
If you want to be happy, be. Be happy for this moment. This moment is your life. There is no other time to be happy than now.
If you want to be happy, practice compassion. If you want others to be happy, practice compassion. No medicine cures what happiness can not.
Success is not the key to happiness; happiness is the key to success.
If you love what you are doing, you are successful.
Don't put the keys to your happiness in someone else's pocket.
If you are you stressed, unhappy, dissatisfied, worried or anxious – then your emotional health needs some serious attention, or your body will start paying the price.

WEDNESDAY **4**

Speak and act with a kind heart

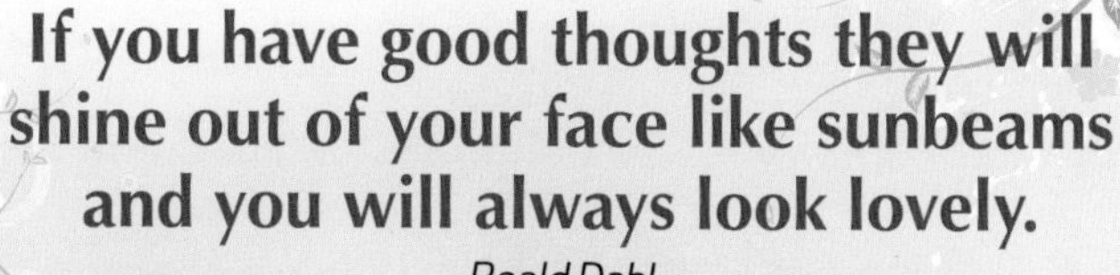

Roald Dahl

THURSDAY **5**

Return what you borrow – better late than never

FRIDAY **6**

Have face-to-face conversations

SATURDAY **7**

Do or say something to brighten someone's day

SUNDAY **8**

Go for a walk and clear your head

I cook with wine, sometimes I even add it to the food.

WC Fields

MONDAY **9**

Stop judging yourself and you will stop judging others

Cauliflower and sweet potato curry

GLUTEN AND DAIRY FREE – FROM MAMA RAE

WHAT YOU WILL NEED

1 head of cauliflower
1 large sweet potato
1 red onion
1 tablespoon coriander
1 tablespoon cumin
1 teaspoon turmeric
1 teaspoon chilli powder
1 5cm piece ginger
2 cloves of garlic
1 400gm can chopped tomatoes
50 ml coconut cream
Coconut oil

THE HOW-TO PART

Break the cauliflower into florets. Peel and chop the sweet potato into cubes. Peel and chop the ginger and the garlic. Heat a large pan on medium heat and add the oil. Add the onion and cook until golden. Add the garlic, ginger, and spices, and cook for 2 – 3 minutes more. You may need to add a little more oil. Add the cauliflower and the sweet potato and stir to coat for 3 – 4 minutes. Add the tomatoes and stir in. Cover with a lid and simmer for 20 minutes, stirring occasionally. Thicken with coconut cream just before serving.

SECRETS FROM MAMA RAE'S KITCHEN

If you don't have any canned tomatoes then use 3 – 4 fresh ones. Pumpkin works just as well as sweet potato in this recipe.

TUESDAY **10**

Smile at the person in the mirror – until they smile back

Whenever sorrow comes, be kind to it. For God has placed a pearl in sorrow's hand.

WEDNESDAY **11**

Balance diet, rest and exercise for optimum health

THURSDAY **12**

Be grateful for those who encourage you

FRIDAY **13**

Get excited about what might go right

I love to shop after a bad relationship. I don't know. I buy a new outfit and it makes me feel better. It just does. Sometimes if I see a really great outfit, I'll break up with someone on purpose.

Rita Rudner

March

SATURDAY **14**

Have a girls' night in

Don't give up trying to do what you really want to do. Where there is love and inspiration, I don't think you can go wrong.

Ella Fitzgerald

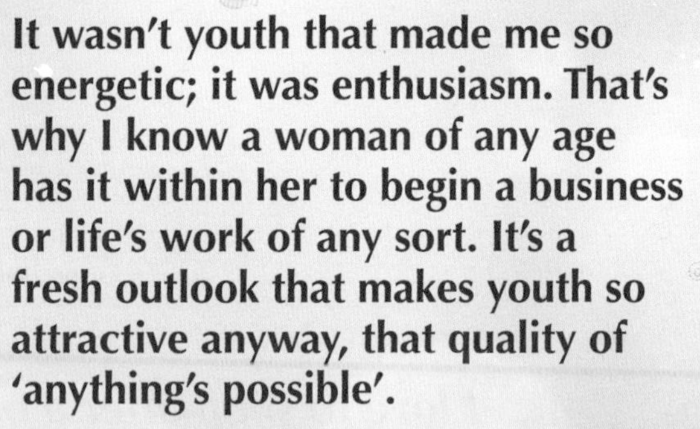

It wasn't youth that made me so energetic; it was enthusiasm. That's why I know a woman of any age has it within her to begin a business or life's work of any sort. It's a fresh outlook that makes youth so attractive anyway, that quality of 'anything's possible'.

Estée Lauder

SUNDAY **15**

Just do it

You'll never find a better sparring partner than adversity.

Golda Meir

MONDAY **16**
Bank holiday

Relax, it's working out just fine

TUESDAY **17**
Happy St. Patricks Day

Use the bright side of your imagination

WEDNESDAY **18**

Find something to appreciate

THURSDAY **19**

For all of us there are many turning points in our life

FRIDAY **20**

Life and times are the world's best teachers

March

All the gods, all the heavens, all the worlds are within us. People say what we're all seeking is a meaning for life. I don't think that's what we're really seeking. I think that what we're seeking is an experience of being alive.

Joseph Campbell

I only believe in fire. Life. Fire. Being myself on fire, I set others on fire. Never death. Fire and life. Les Jeux.

Anais Nin

SATURDAY **21**

Go on a picnic

SUNDAY **22**

Let go of resistance ... it's easier to swim with the current

In order to be truly creative, you must have the attitude of a beginner. To be a beginner means to maintain innocence and receptivity, for it is only in this way that we can truly and quickly develop our knowledge.

Amma

MONDAY **23**

Cast off your childhood fears

TUESDAY **24**

Resist the pressure to add more pressure

WEDNESDAY **25**

You are perfect just as you are

THURSDAY **26**

Never go against your core values

FRIDAY **27**

Leave others happier for having met you

SATURDAY **28**

When we learn something positive we grow bigger

SUNDAY **29**

There is no harm in settling for contentment

MONDAY **30**

Remain warm and approachable

TUESDAY **31**

There is nothing to be gained by giving grief

BUCKET LIST for April

Courage MONTH

Courage starts with showing up and letting ourselves be seen.

Brené Brown

You gain strength, courage and confidence by every experience in which you really stop to look fear in the face. You are able to say to yourself 'I have lived through this horror. I can take the next thing that comes along.' You must do the thing you think you cannot do.

Eleanor Roosevelt

If you don't risk anything, you risk even more.

Erica Jong

If you don't get out of the box you've been raised in, you won't understand how much bigger the world is.

Angelina Jolie

WEDNESDAY **1**

Your life is a mirror of your consistent thoughts

THURSDAY **2**

We reap what we sow

FRIDAY **3**

Spend time with enthusiastic people

SATURDAY **4**

Value your unique strengths

You can't be that kid standing at the top of the waterslide, overthinking it. You have to go down the chute.

Tina Fey

The mother lioness doesn't tell her cub, stay small and hide so the wolves don't get you. She says, grow up, toughen up, this is real life and only the strong survive.

Never have more children than you have car windows.

Erma Bombeck

SUNDAY **5**

Prepare well, then go with the flow

April

You can never leave footprints in the sands of time if you are walking on tiptoe or dragging your feet.

MONDAY **6**

Be willing to admit when you're wrong

TUESDAY **7**

Peace comes from within – do not seek it without

WEDNESDAY **8**

Often silence is the best answer

THURSDAY **9**

Be happy for no reason

The way we talk to our children becomes their inner voice.

Peggy O'Mara

FRIDAY **10**
Good Friday

Avoid cynicism and mediocrity

SATURDAY **11**

Take the dog for a walk

SUNDAY **12**
Easter Sunday

Celebrate the miracles of life

Step out of the history that is holding you back. Step into the new story you are willing to create.

Oprah Winfrey

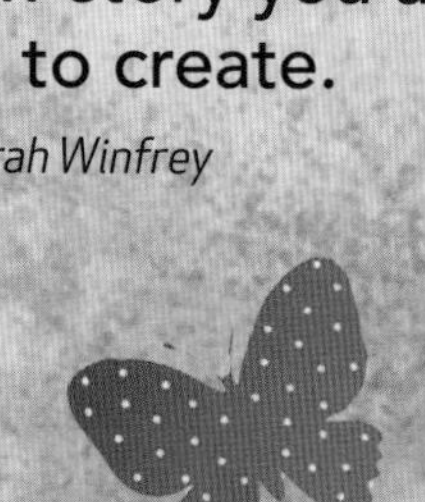

Above all, be the heroine of your life, not the victim.

Nora Ephron

MONDAY **13**
Easter Monday

What are you avoiding?

TUESDAY **14**

We see what we focus on

WEDNESDAY **15**

Enthusiasm for life reflects positively on your health

THURSDAY **16**

The past is done, leave it behind you

Security is mostly a superstition. It does not exist in nature, nor do the children of men as a whole experience it. Avoiding danger is no safer in the long run than outright exposure. Life is either a daring adventure, or nothing.

Helen Keller

It is our choices that show us who we truly are, far more than our abilities.

FRIDAY **17**

Get comfortable with journaling

SATURDAY **18**

Don't suffer unnecessarily

SUNDAY **19**

Guilt is unproductive

Too many women in too many countries speak the same language, of silence.

Hillary Clinton

Nutty chocolate cake

GLUTEN AND REFINED SUGAR FREE – FROM MAMA RAE

WHAT YOU WILL NEED

1 cup coconut oil
4 tablespoons chia seeds
3 tablespoons milk
1 cup coconut sugar
240gm gluten-free flour
1 cup cacao
2 teaspoons baking powder
1/3 cup peanut butter

THE HOW-TO PART

Turn oven on to 180 degrees. Put the melted oil, chia seeds and milk in a bowl and stand for 15-20 minutes for the chia to swell. Sift the flour, cacao, and baking powder in another bowl. Add the coconut oil mix to the flour and gently fold in until mixed. Pour into a lined 20 cm round cake tin. Spoon the peanut butter over the top of the batter. With a knife, gently cut the peanut butter through the top of the cake. Put into the oven and bake for 20 – 30 minutes. Leave in tin for 20-30 minutes before cutting.

SECRETS FROM MAMA RAE'S KITCHEN

If you are allergic to peanuts then use another nut butter.
You could ice this cake with chocolate if you wanted for an extra chocolate shot. Melt 1/3 cup coconut butter/oil, 1/3 cup cacao, and ¼ cup maple syrup. Pour over the cake and chill in the refrigerator for 15 minutes or until the chocolate is set.

Life shrinks or expands in proportion to one's courage.

Anais Nin

MONDAY **20**

Stay true to your core values

TUESDAY **21**

Be at peace with the world

It isn't where you came from,
it's where you're going that counts.

Ella Fitzgerald

WEDNESDAY **22**

Don't confuse busy with productive

THURSDAY **23**

Actively pursue what is important to you

FRIDAY **24**

Make your health a priority

SATURDAY **25**

Take one step in the direction you want to go

SUNDAY **26**

Greet people with enthusiasm

He suffers more than necessary, who suffers before it is necessary.

Seneca

MONDAY **27**

Be at ease with your circumstances

TUESDAY **28**

Children learn more by example than instruction

WEDNESDAY **29**

Don't assume anything, ever!

THURSDAY **30**

Everyone just wants to be accepted

If you can't get rid of the skeleton in your closet, you'd best teach it to dance.

George Bernard Shaw

I will smile at friend and foe alike and make every effort to find, in him or her, a quality to praise, now that I realise the deepest yearning of human nature is the craving to be appreciated.

Og Mandino

FRIDAY **1**

Value your friendships

May

Food, love, career, and mothers, the four major guilt groups.

Cathy G

SATURDAY **2**

Join a dance class

SUNDAY **3**

Thank your parents – they did their best

ON RESILIENCE

■ Realise that each human being has a built in capacity for recuperation, repair and restoration. ■ Nurture the regenerative and restorative forces with you. ■ Assume responsibility for the quality of your own life and your own journey. ■ Acknowledge your triumphs and express gratitude for your strength. ■ Accept your defeats and express your willingness to try again. ■ Utilise laughter to create a mood in which the other positive emotions can be put to work for yourself and those around you – we're all in this together. ■ Have confidence in your ability to feel, love, hope, believe and trust.
■ No matter how you feel, get up, dress up, show up and step up.

MONDAY **4**
Bank holiday

Have a bath by candlelight

You are already OK, a perfect and unique manifestation of the universe in human form. Some of you have been taught to believe otherwise. You were born into a world that has taught you to hide and suppress who you really are, in order to be approved of by your group, so it is understandable that you are disconnected from your true self and continually seek approval from others. However, they are doing the very same thing, and seeking approval from you!

Accepting who and how you are is the resolution to the conflict and pain you feel because you think you are not enough, that you are not OK as you are, that you are not good enough, or pretty enough, or smart enough.

You are perfect just as you are, for what you are here for. The struggle is to accept this, and when you get it, you discover who you truly are, and what your life is for, and you begin to come out of your shell, to stop hiding, to stop pretending to be OK and you begin to express yourself fully and freely – and you begin to shine!

I have always been delighted at the prospect of a new day, a fresh try, one more start, with perhaps a bit of magic waiting somewhere behind the morning.

JB Priestly

TUESDAY **5**

Notice your communication style

WEDNESDAY **6**

Develop a regular exercise programme

THURSDAY **7**

Schedule a date night

FRIDAY **8**

Allow yourself to wonder at the miracle of it all

ON SISTERS

A sister is a little bit of childhood that can never be lost.
A sister is both your mirror and your reflection.
A sister smiles when you tell stories for she knows where the decoration has been added.
For there is no friend like a sister, in calm or stormy weather, to cheer one on the tedious way, to fetch one if one goes astray, to lift one if one totters down, to straighten up your tilted crown, to strengthen whilst one stands.
How the hell do you sum up your sister in three minutes? She's your twin and your polar opposite. She's your constant companion and your competition. She's your best friend and the biggest bitch in the world. She's everything you wish you could be and everything you wish you weren't.
If you don't understand how a woman could both love her sister dearly and want to wring her neck at the same time, then you were probably an only child.
Sister is our first friend and our second mother.

One is not born, but rather becomes, a woman.

Simone de Beauvoir

SATURDAY **9**

A picture paints a thousand words

SUNDAY **10**

Visit your parents

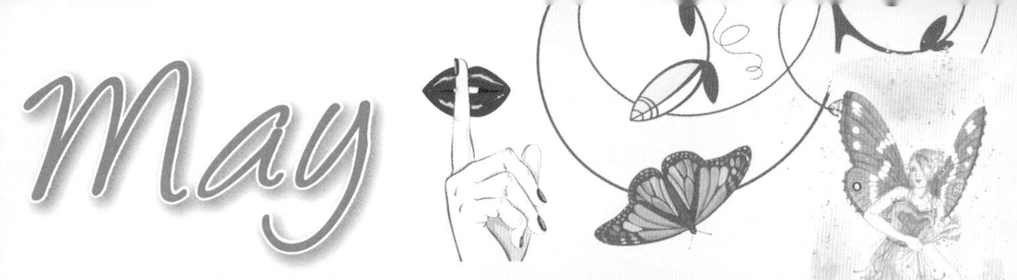

The secret to living the life of your dreams is to start living the life of your dreams today, in every little way you possibly can.

Mike Dooley

MONDAY **11**

Connect with an old friend

TUESDAY **12**

Write a love letter

WEDNESDAY **13**

Be interested in lots of things

THURSDAY **14**

Plan a holiday

The truth is that there is no actual stress or anxiety in the world; it's your thoughts that create these false beliefs. You can't package stress, touch it, or see it. There are only people engaged in stressful thinking.

Wayne Dyer

FRIDAY **15**

Don't put your life on hold

SATURDAY **16**

In your heart you know

SUNDAY **17**

Use the good china

Bad days call for foods that are bad for your butt.

HM Ward

May

HOW TO HAVE A GOOD NIGHT'S SLEEP

Stick to a consistent sleep-wake schedule.
Reduce caffeine intake and avoid it six hours before bedtime.
Prepare for sleep – dim light, soft music.
Let your brain slow down
Avoid the bright lights (screens) that keep you awake.
Wish your loved ones 'good night'.
Apologise. Do not go to bed upset.
Write your to do list for tomorrow
If you can't sleep, don't linger in bed – get out and do something to make you tired, such as reading or some gentle stretching.
Don't linger in bed in the morning, and don't hit snooze.
Get up, go about your day, hit your pillow at bedtime, at which point your sleep drive will be strong and you will reap the benefit of deep restorative sleep.

MONDAY **18**

Organise your children

TUESDAY **19**

Be flexible

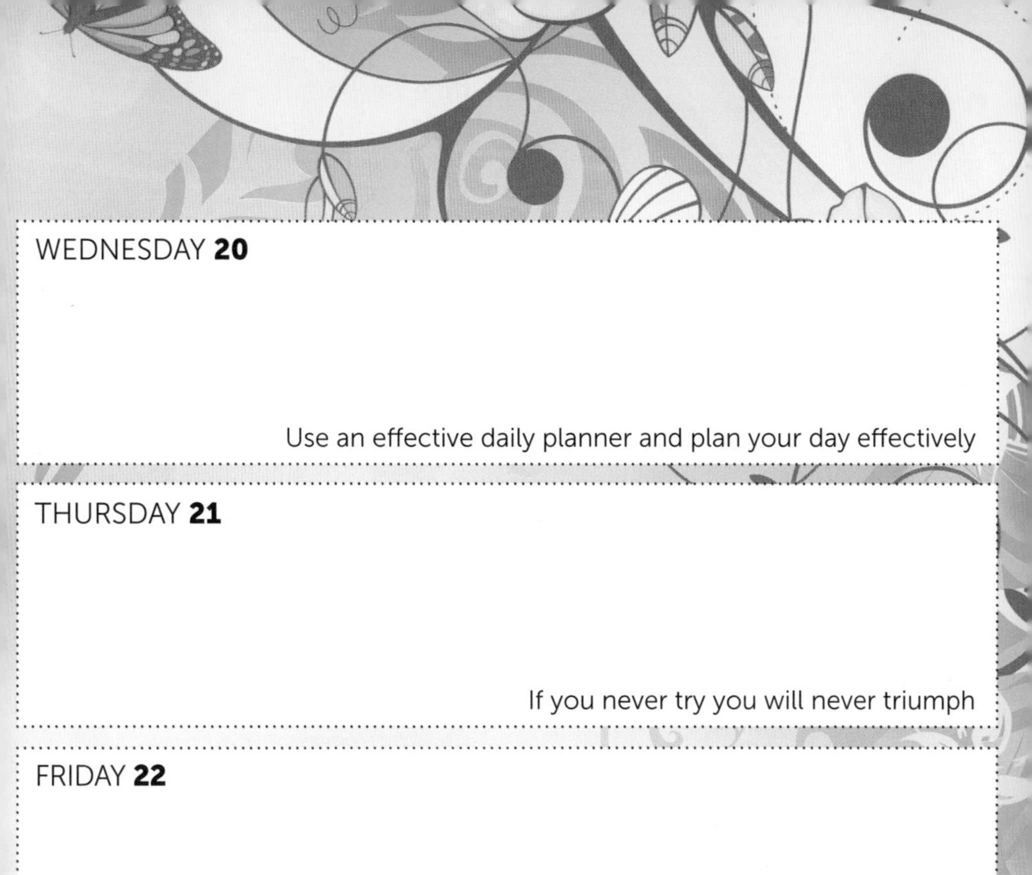

WEDNESDAY **20**

Use an effective daily planner and plan your day effectively

THURSDAY **21**

If you never try you will never triumph

FRIDAY **22**

Change the world by your example, not your opinion

SATURDAY **23**

Volunteer for a local charity

SUNDAY **24**

Go on a bike ride

Take time for happiness. Allow yourself to enjoy life, fun, and relaxation. Be thankful for what you have, and enjoy it.

MONDAY **25**

Don't wait for opportunity, create it

TUESDAY **26**

Make your idea happen

WEDNESDAY **27**

Keep the dream alive

What you have learned from experience is worth much more than gold. If you have a house, it may burn down. Any kind of possession can be lost. But your experience is yours forever. Keep it and find a way to use it.

Somaly Mam

Carrot slaw

FROM MAMA RAE

WHAT YOU WILL NEED

3 small carrots
1 medium beetroot
1 medium apple

THE HOW-TO PART

Grate the carrots, beetroot and the apple. Stir so that the apple, carrots, and beetroot are evenly mixed. Put into a serving bowl and decorate with chopped walnuts and/or parsley.

SECRETS FROM MAMA RAE'S KITCHEN

This is delicious if you add a small grated swede or turnip. No dressing is necessary as there is lots of juice in the apple, beetroot and carrots.

Be creative. Spend some time learning new things, like a new language or skill. Even just working in your garden can help you relax and feel satisfied.

Adopt an animal. Pets offer fun, relaxation, and a whole lot of love. They can encourage you to exercise, and tear your attention away from stressful activities.

THURSDAY **28**

Be great with people

FRIDAY **29**

Discover the pleasure of giving

We have a new phenomenon which is being frazzled, which is stress about stress. What's killing us is our own thinking.
Ruby Wax

You know ... you can TALK about something, THINK about something, DREAM about something ... But do you know when stuff gets real? It's when you COMMIT and DO something – buy the tickets (or write the resignation letter or file for divorce or ask for the raise or register for the class or make the dreaded phone call or ____ fill in your blank). It is action that has the power to change everything.
Ashlie Woods

I hate housework! You make the beds, you do the dishes and six months later you have to start all over again.
Joan Rivers

SATURDAY **30**

Spend time with those you care about

SUNDAY **31**

Take time out

BUCKET LIST for June

Discovery MONTH

Read first the best books. The important thing for you to know is not how much you know, but the quality of what you know.

Desiderius Erasmus

Imagination is not only the uniquely human capacity to envision that which is not, and, therefore, the foundation of all invention and innovation. In its arguably most transformative and revelatory capacity, it is the power that enables us to empathise with humans whose experiences we have never shared.

JK Rowling

June

Beware of monotony; it's the mother of all the deadly sins.

Edith Wharton

MONDAY **1**
Bank holiday

Keep your own house in order

TUESDAY **2**

Aim above the mark to hit the mark

WEDNESDAY **3**

Mistakes are forgivable

THURSDAY **4**

A change is as good as a rest

THE AWAKENING

A time comes in your life when you finally get it! When in the midst of all your fears and insanity you stop dead in your tracks and somewhere the inner voice inside your head cries out ENOUGH. Enough fighting and crying and struggling to hold on. And like a child settling down after an exhausting 'tantrum', you begin to look at the world through new eyes.
This is your awakening.

You realise that it's time to stop hoping and waiting for something to change or for happiness, safety and security to come galloping over the next horizon.

You come to terms with the fact that he is not Prince Charming and you are not Cinderella and in the real world there aren't always fairy-tale endings. You awaken to the fact that you are not perfect and that not everyone will always love, appreciate or approve of who or what you are. You realise the importance and necessity of championing yourself and in the process, a sense that any guarantee of 'happy ever after' must begin with you. A new-found confidence is born "If it is to be, it's up to me" You realise that complaining and blaming other people for what's wrong with your life gives you no power. People don't always say what they mean or mean what they say, not everyone will always be there for you, and the only thing you can really count on is the unexpected.
You have what you need to stand on your own and take care of yourself and in the process a sense of safety and security is born of self-reliance.
You stop judging and pointing fingers and begin to see and accept people as they are. You overlook their shortcomings and human frailties and in the process a sense of peace and contentment is born of forgiveness.

You start to open up to new worlds and different points of view.
You begin reassessing and redefining who you are and what you really stand for.

You see the difference between wanting and needing and begin to discard the beliefs and opinions you have outgrown.

You discover that it in giving that we truly receive and there is power and glory in creating and contributing and you can stop manoeuvring through life merely as a 'consumer' looking for your next 'fix'.

You learn that principles such as honesty and integrity are not the outdated ideals of a bygone era but the mortar that holds together the foundation upon which you must build a life.

You learn that you don't know everything; it's not your job to save the world and you can't teach a pig to sing!

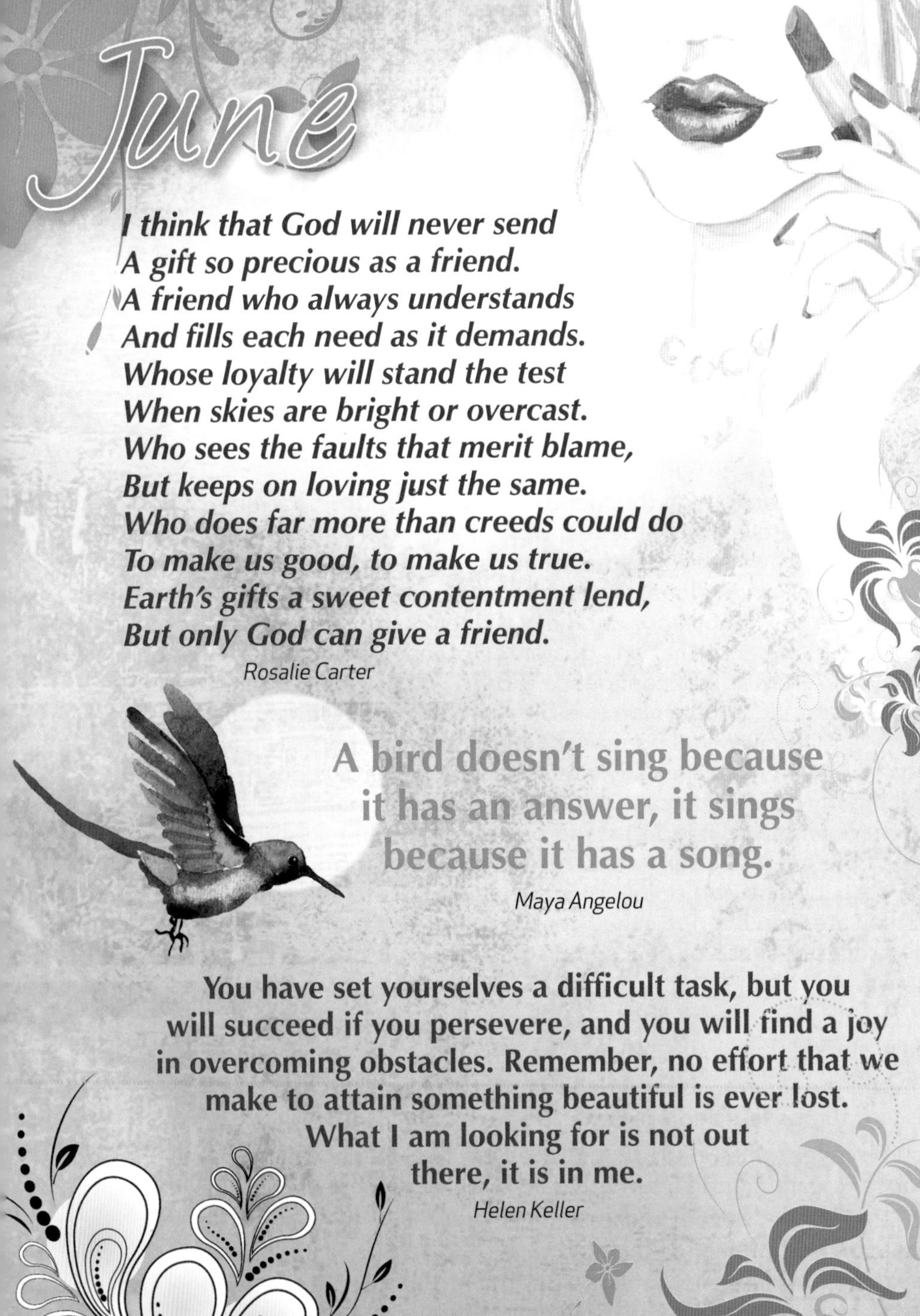

June

I think that God will never send
A gift so precious as a friend.
A friend who always understands
And fills each need as it demands.
Whose loyalty will stand the test
When skies are bright or overcast.
Who sees the faults that merit blame,
But keeps on loving just the same.
Who does far more than creeds could do
To make us good, to make us true.
Earth's gifts a sweet contentment lend,
But only God can give a friend.

Rosalie Carter

A bird doesn't sing because it has an answer, it sings because it has a song.

Maya Angelou

You have set yourselves a difficult task, but you will succeed if you persevere, and you will find a joy in overcoming obstacles. Remember, no effort that we make to attain something beautiful is ever lost. What I am looking for is not out there, it is in me.

Helen Keller

FRIDAY **5**

Suffering does not guarantee better results

SATURDAY **6**

Be proud of your accomplishments

SUNDAY **7**

Cheer someone up

**Life is amazing. And then it's awful.
And then it's amazing again. And in between
the amazing and awful it's ordinary and mundane
and routine. Breathe in the amazing, hold on
through the awful, and relax and exhale during the
ordinary. That's just living a heart-breaking,
soul-healing, amazing, awful, ordinary life.
And it's breathtakingly beautiful.**

LR Knost

MONDAY **8**

Fight for what is good

TUESDAY **9**

Life is an exciting business

WEDNESDAY **10**

A good beginning makes a good ending

THURSDAY **11**

You will find what you look for

FRIDAY **12**

You are the source of your own happiness

I used to be Snow White, but I drifted.

Mae West

SATURDAY **13**

Let your work enrich your spirit and your spirit enrich your work

SUNDAY **14**

We each have our faults

Life is hard. After all, it kills you.

Katherine Hepburn

Salmon patties

GLUTEN, FREE, DAIRY FREE AND EGG FREE – FROM MAMA RAE

WHAT YOU WILL NEED

2 tins wild caught salmon
1 ½ cups cooked sweet potato
2 large spring onions
½ cup fresh coriander
2 teaspoons herb salt
2 tablespoons chia seeds
4 tablespoons gluten-free flour

THE HOW-TO PART

Preheat oven to 150 degrees. Chop spring onions and coriander Mix all ingredients except salmon (add last) and the flour. Put the flour in a bowl. Make patties, dip in flour and put onto tray. Bake for 35-40 minutes.

SECRETS FROM MAMA RAE'S KITCHEN

You can use pumpkin for the sweet potato and onion instead of spring onions. Parsley will work in place of the coriander. You can replace the chia with two eggs.

I didn't ask for it to be over, but then again, I never asked for it to begin. For that is the way it is with life, as some of the most beautiful days come completely by chance. And even the most beautiful days eventually have their sunsets.

MONDAY **15**

Help others to succeed

TUESDAY **16**

Remind your friends of their worth, and yourself of your own

WEDNESDAY **17**

Better a friendly refusal than an unwilling promise

THURSDAY **18**

Join a book club

Love: a wildly misunderstood although highly desirable malfunction of the heart which weakens the brain, causes eyes to sparkle, cheeks to glow, blood pressure to rise and the lips to pucker.

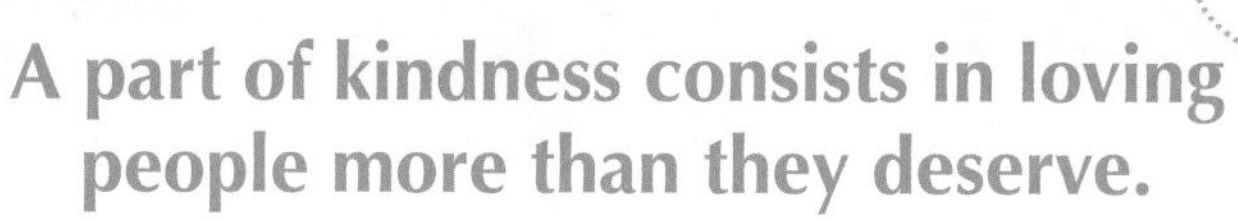

A part of kindness consists in loving people more than they deserve.

Joseph Joubert

FRIDAY **19**

Education begins at home

SATURDAY **20**

Common sense is rarely common

SUNDAY **21**
Father's Day

Be in awe of what you are capable of

Every mother hopes that her daughter will marry a better man than she did, and is convinced that her son will never find a wife as good as his father did.

Martin Andersen Nexo

Do one thing every day that scares you.

Eleanor Roosevelt

I love deadlines. I like the whooshing sound they make as they fly by.
Douglas Adams

Some mistakes are too much fun to make only once.

MONDAY **22**

Show respect for others time – don't be late!

TUESDAY **23**

A happy heart makes the face cheerful

WEDNESDAY **24**

Do not become a to-do list

THURSDAY **25**

Be content with a little

Life is an opportunity, explore it.
Life is beauty, admire it.
Life is a dream, realise it.
Life is a challenge, meet it.
Life is a duty, complete it.
Life is game, play it.
Life is a promise, fulfill it.
Life is a sorrow, overcome it.
Life is a song, sing it.
Life is a struggle, accept it.
Life is a tragedy, confront it.
Life is an adventure, dare it.
Life is luck, make it.
Life is precious – do not damage it. Live it.
Fight for it. Fight for your dreams and your desires.
You are worth it and you have the right to enjoy it.

FRIDAY **26**

The majority is often mistaken

SATURDAY **27**

Visualise your goals

SUNDAY **28**

You can learn something from everything

June

MONDAY **29**

Have a say in how your life goes

TUESDAY **30**

Be original – even eccentric

Do not listen to those who weep and complain, for their disease is contagious.

Og Mandino

All careers go up and down like friendships, like marriages, like anything else, and you can't bat a thousand all the time.

Julie Andrews

Trust is the glue of life. It is the most essential ingredient in effective communication. It is the foundational principle that holds all relationships.

Stephen Covey

BUCKET LIST *for July*

Nurturing *MONTH*

Make allowances for your friends' imperfections as readily as you do for your own.

H Jackson Brown

WEDNESDAY **1**

Don't gossip

July

Chocolate mousse

DAIRY, EGG, AND GLUTEN FREE – FROM MAMA RAE

WHAT YOU WILL NEED

1/2 can coconut cream
½ cup almond milk
3 tablespoons cacao powdered
3 tablespoons chia seeds
2 tablespoon maple syrup
½ teaspoon vanilla

THE HOW-TO PART

Add all ingredients to a bowl and whisk together. Pour into a serving dish. Chill until set – it will take about 2 ½ – 3 hours. Decorate with berries and shaved coconut.

SECRETS FROM MAMA RAE'S KITCHEN

You can turn this into a tart by making a crust of 1 cup of nuts, 1 cup of coconut, 4 medjool dates and ¼ cup of coconut oil. Process and put into a 20 cm tin. Chill till set and then pour mousse into base and return to the refrigerator for 3 hours or until set. Beautiful served with berries, chopped nuts, and shaved coconut. You can add 2-3 drops of peppermint or orange oil. Serve with fresh fruit or marinated orange or mandarin segments.
If you like it sweeter then add more maple syrup or whatever sweetener you are using.

THE HEALTH-FOOD DINER

**No sprouted wheat and soya shoots
And Brussels in a cake,
Carrot straw and spinach raw,
(Today, I need a steak).
Not thick brown rice and rice pilaw
Or mushrooms creamed on toast,
Turnips mashed and parsnips hashed,
(I'm dreaming of a roast).
Health-food folks around the world
Are thinned by anxious zeal,
They look for help in seafood kelp
(I count on breaded veal).
No smoking signs,
raw mustard greens,
Zucchini by the ton,
Uncooked kale and bodies frail
Are sure to make me run to
Loins of pork and chicken thighs
And standing rib, so prime,
Pork chops brown and fresh ground round
(I crave them all the time).
Irish stews and boiled corned beef
and hot dogs by the scores,
or any place that saves a space
For smoking carnivores.**

Maya Angelou

It is not alone the fact that women have generally had to spend most of their strength in caring for others that has handicapped them in individual effort; but also that they have almost universally had to care wholly for themselves.

Anna Garlin

I'd rather regret the things I've done, than regret the things I haven't done.

Lucille Ball

When I eventually met Mr Right, I had no idea that his first name was Always.

Rita Rudner

THURSDAY **2**

Be a lifelong learner

FRIDAY **3**

The best fighter is never angry

SATURDAY **4**

Either you run the day or the day runs you

SUNDAY **5**

Be respectful of others' opinions

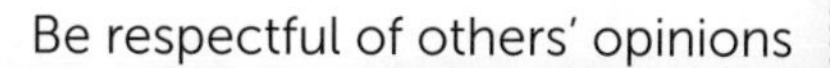

MONDAY **6**

What you believe determines everything

What do you do when faced with 24/7 connectivity?

Establish boundaries and planned time off.
Use technology to enhance your life, not distract you from it.
A 'flexible schedule' doesn't mean 'always working'.
Have the tough conversation with your employer (even if that's you!).
Turn off your screen and tune in to your life.

TUESDAY **7**

Be here now

WEDNESDAY **8**

A problem shared is a problem halved

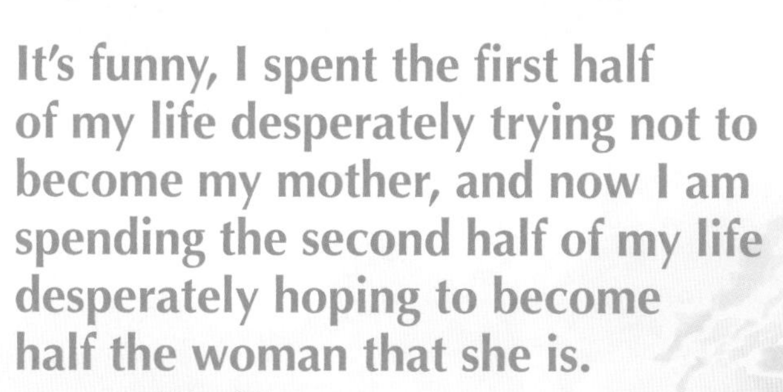

It's funny, I spent the first half of my life desperately trying not to become my mother, and now I am spending the second half of my life desperately hoping to become half the woman that she is.

Helen C Escott

THURSDAY **9**

Empower others to be great

FRIDAY **10**

Beliefs are not facts

SATURDAY **11**

The hand that rocks the cradle rules the world

SUNDAY **12**

Have a clear vision of your desired future

Not all wounds are visible. Walk gently in the lives of others.

Eleanor Roosevelt

MONDAY **13**

Confidence grows with action

TUESDAY **14**

Ease is a function of choice

WEDNESDAY **15**

The dinner table is a great place to learn

THURSDAY **16**

Avoid people who are constantly negative

Negative people need drama like oxygen. Stay positive, it'll take their breath away.

Tony Gaskins

I know God will not give me anything I can't handle. I just wish he didn't trust me so much.

Mother Teresa

FRIDAY **17**

To err is human, to forgive divine

SATURDAY **18**

Discover hidden passions

SUNDAY **19**

Spoil your partner, not your children

Chairs were created because someone, somewhere, wanted to solve a big problem: sitting on rocks causes sore bottoms.

Bill Burnett

Only as high as I reach, can I grow.
Only as far as I see, can I go.
Only as much as I live, can I be.
Only as much as I do, can I know.

The number one reason people fail in life is because they listen to their friends, family, and neighbours.

Napoleon Hill

MONDAY **20**

Patience is a wonderful virtue

POSITIVE AFFIRMATIONS FOR A FULFILLED LIFE

I am unique and valuable ■ I am worthy of love ■ I am vital and full of energy ■ I am beautiful and loving and loved ■ I am safe in the universe ■ I am open to the abundance that awaits ■ I am free to love myself, to love life and to love the world ■ I accept myself as I am ■ I accept others as they are ■ I forgive myself so I can be free ■ I forgive others so I can be free ■ I let go of the past that limits my future ■ I let go all thoughts of not being good enough ■ I leave behind all feelings of unworthiness ■ I change thoughts of hurt to thoughts that heal ■ I acknowledge and appreciate all my blessings ■ I express gratitude for all that I am and all that I have ■ I smile at the world and the world smiles back ■ I see the beauty that surrounds me ■ I acknowledge the beauty that is within me ■ I love and accept my family ■ I honour my friends ■ I value my home and my comforts ■ I respect my body and take good care of it ■ I love life and life loves me back ■ I radiate love and it returns to me multiplied ■ I know I can achieve my dreams ■ I deserve all the goodness that life has to offer ■ I trust in the process of life ■ I promise myself I will live my life to my fullest potential ■ I am at peace with my life ■ I am at peace with others ■ I am at peace with myself.

ALL IS WELL

TUESDAY **21**

Saying thank you is more than good manners

History is filled with stories of individuals who dated a new era in their lives from the reading of a single book.

Og Mandino

WEDNESDAY **22**

Sooner or later, everything new becomes old

THURSDAY **23**

Do what you can, with what you have, where you are

FRIDAY **24**

Everything has its wonders

SATURDAY **25**

There is no love without forgiveness

SUNDAY **26**

People are as they are

11 MOOD-BOOSTING FOODS

YOU NEED TO HAVE IN YOUR KITCHEN

1. Brazil nuts are a source of selenium – good for depression irritability, anxiety and tiredness. Have three brazil nuts per day snack with a banana, or sprinkle chopped on salads.

2. Oily fish is a source of omega-3 fatty acids. Eating salmon, mackerel and sardines improves your mood by keeping brain cells flexible. Try at least one serving of mackerel (140g) a week for a brain-boosting breakfast or lunch.

3. Oats are an effective mood booster as slow release energy into the bloodstream keeps blood sugar and mood stable. Also contain mood-boosting selenium. Half a cup of porridge with honey, nuts and yoghurt is a great way to start the day.

4. Bananas are a source of tryptophan, vitamins A, B6 and C, fibre, potassium, phosphorous, iron and carbohydrate. B6 helps convert the tryptophan into serotonin, boosting your mood and aiding sleep. Eat one medium-sized banana each day.

5. Lentils are complex carbohydrates that increase brain production of the feel-good neurotransmitter serotonin, resulting in a calmer, happier state of mind with less anxiety. They also help stabilise blood sugar levels, keeping your mood even. Plus, they're high in folate can help boost your iron levels. Try half a cup of lentils in homemade soups or stews. (Soak them for a few hours before cooking).

6. Chicken and turkey breast help the body to make serotonin and the hormone melatonin which regulate sleep. Lean poultry also contains tyrosine, which can help you avoid feeling blue. Use them a few times a week in soups, sandwiches or on their own with vegetables.

7. Spinach and broccoli have important B vitamins including folate, vitamins B3, B6 and B12. Eating leafy green vegetables will help keep your levels up. A cup of cooked spinach provides nearly 30% of your RDA of a few B vitamins, so add it to stir-fry and soups, or make a raw spinach salad for lunch.

8. Water is extremely important for our bodies to function properly. Even the smallest degree of water loss can impair our physical and mental wellbeing. One to two litres per day is recommended. Start the day with freshly boiled water and a slice of lemon, or add a fresh sprig of mint, cucumber or strawberries to a jug of cold water to jazz it up.

9. Cereal with calcium has been shown to help reduce your levels of stress. A cup of fortified cereal can provide up to a third of your RDA of calcium.

10. Dark chocolate causes the brain to release endorphins and boost serotonin levels and produce less stress hormones decreasing anxiety. A couple of squares is all it takes (70% cocoa), so try not to hoover up the whole bar!

11. Oysters are high in zinc, which is essential for energy production and brain health. They are rich in tyrosine – needed to enhance mental function and elevate your mood. Three oysters will give you more than 100% of your RDA of zinc.

Best way to get rid of kitchen odours: Eat out.

Phyllis Diller

Success does not consist in never making mistakes but in never making the same one a second time.

George Bernard Shaw

MONDAY **27**

Be in charge of your schedule

TUESDAY **28**

Be aware of the destination but focus on the journey

WEDNESDAY **29**

The best way is always through

THURSDAY **30**

Be grateful for where you are and excited about where you're going

FRIDAY **31**

Don't burn your candle at both ends

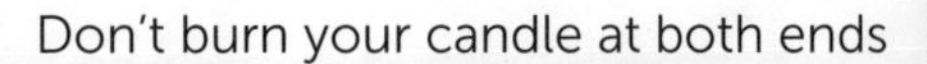

BUCKET LIST for August

Gratitude MONTH

We are, each of us, a miracle. Within every one of us, the pilot light of hope never dies.

Og Mandino

You don't have to be great to start, but you have to start to be great.

Zig Ziglar

MY YOUNGER DAYS

When I was in my younger days,
I weighed a few pounds less,
I needn't hold my tummy in
to wear a belted dress.
But now that I am older,
I've set my body free;
There's the comfort of elastic
Where once my waist would be.
Inventor of those high-heeled shoes
My feet have not forgiven;
I have to wear a nine now,
But used to wear a seven.
And how about those pantyhose-
They're sized by weight, you see,
So how come when I put them on
The crotch is at my knee?
I need to wear these glasses
As the print's been getting smaller;
And it wasn't very long ago
I know that I was taller.
Though my hair has turned to gray
and my skin no longer fits,
On the inside, I'm the same old me,
It's the outside's changed a bit.

Maya Angelou

SATURDAY **1**

Let go of what you cannot control

SUNDAY **2**

Won't is a word of resistance; Can't is a word of defeat

A FEW IMPORTANT RULES TO TEACH YOUR DAUGHTERS (SONS NOT EXEMPT!)

1. It's okay to cry when you're hurt. But wash your face, and get up off the floor when you're done. You don't belong down there.
2. You are a person, you do not need another person, but you can absolutely enjoy your life with a good one.
3. Happiness is not a permanent state. Wholeness is. Don't confuse these.
4. Never walk through an alley alone.
5. 'Can't' is a cop-out.
6. Hold your heroes to a high standard. Be your own hero.
7. If you can't smile with your eyes, don't smile. Insincerity is nothing to aspire to.
8. Stay true to yourself always.
9. Your body, your rules, your responsibility.
10. If you have an opinion, you'd better know why.
11. Practice your passions.
12. Ask for what you want. The worst thing they can say is no.
13. Wish on stars, and then get to work to make them happen.
14. Stay as loving and as lovable as you are.
15. Say Please, Thank You, and Pardon Me, whenever the situation warrants it.
16. Reserve "I'm sorry" for when you truly are!
17. Question everything ... except your own intuition.
18. You are wonderful! If someone makes you feel less, walk away. You deserve better.
19. No matter where you are, you can always come home.
20. Be happy and remember your roots.
21. Say what you mean and mean what you say.
22. Be kind; treat others how you would like them to treat you.
23. If in doubt, remember whose daughter you are and straighten your crown.

August

Try walking forward while looking over your shoulder and see how far you get. The same goes for life. Look forward!

Martin Henderson

Your pain is the breaking of the shell that encloses your understanding. And if you could keep your heart in wonder at the daily miracles of your life, your pain would not seem less wondrous than your joy.

Khalil Gibran

MONDAY **3**
Bank holiday

Seek out the truth of the matter

TUESDAY **4**

Hold on to what you value

If God wanted us to bend over, he'd put diamonds on the floor.

Joan Rivers

THE EMPTY CHAIR

**I forgot to love myself today, when pain was all around.
I forgot to pay attention to the courage I had found.
I forgot that many love me, much more than I can tell.
I forgot that this is a time for peace and love as well.
I forgot that sadness on one day doesn't count for all the years.
I forgot how much a simple hug could allay so many fears.
I forgot that on my forehead once a loving kiss was placed.
I forgot that there are many loves, and each one has its place.
I forgot to love myself today and saw the flowers there.
I forgot it was a special thing to be in someone's prayer.
I forgot that I am blessed with life and many go too quick.
I forgot the flower would cease to be once it has been picked.
I forgot that life's in moments and beauty doesn't last.
I forgot that years can pass us by so very, very fast.
I forgot the words of poems and love-songs we would sing.
And remembered that friendship, love and gratitude is
truly everything.**

WEDNESDAY **5**

Desire is the starting point of all achievement

THURSDAY **6**

Always keep the bigger picture in mind

What you do makes a difference, and you have to decide what kind of difference you want to make.

Jane Goodall

FRIDAY **7**

Think positive thoughts and speak positive words – and notice positive results

SATURDAY **8**

Forgive yourself for your mistakes and move on

Without Sunday, I wouldn't know when to put on the brakes of a hurtling life.

Byron Pulsifer

When we habitually set aside time to be quiet and simply listen, a new awareness develops.

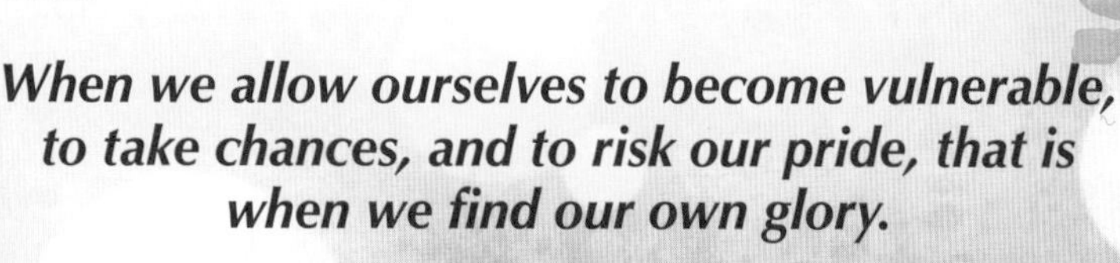

When we allow ourselves to become vulnerable, to take chances, and to risk our pride, that is when we find our own glory.

Richard Corman

SUNDAY **9**

Stay connected with your bigger vision

August

A good compromise is one where everybody makes a contribution.

Angela Merkel

MONDAY **10**

Take one day at a time

TUESDAY **11**

Have a goal and a plan to reach it

WEDNESDAY **12**

Those who fling mud generally lose ground

THURSDAY **13**

Let others know what you can be trusted for – in word and deed

I choose to make the rest of my life the best of my life.

Louise Hay

FRIDAY **14**

Life is a journey and every step is to be taken

SATURDAY **15**

Appearances can be deceptive

The question isn't who is going to let me; it's who is going to stop me.

Ayn Rand

Snack balls

GLUTEN, DAIRY, AND REFINED SUGAR FREE – FROM MAMA RAE

WHAT YOU WILL NEED

8 dates
1/3 cup walnuts
2 tablespoons cacao
1/3 cup coconut
¼ teaspoon cinnamon

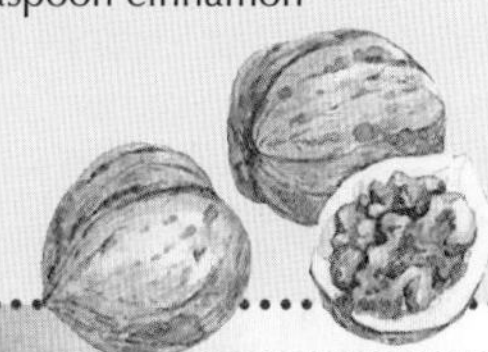

THE HOW-TO PART

Put all the ingredients into the food processor. Process until the mixture is crumbly and sticky. Roll into balls. Store in a sealed container in the refrigerator.

SECRETS FROM MAMA RAE'S KITCHEN

Substitute any other nuts for the walnuts. Add ¼ cup of chopped dried apricots or cranberries for something different. You can take out the cacao and add a tablespoon of lemon juice. Maybe start with 2 teaspoons, taste and add more little by little. If you want a sweeter bliss ball then add some more dates.

SUNDAY **16**

Don't be afraid to dig deep – buried treasure is rarely near the surface

August

Troubles, like babies, grow large by nursing.

Lady Holland

MONDAY **17**

Live true to your higher values

TUESDAY **18**

We shall not pass this way again

WEDNESDAY **19**

When you're upset, you're upset

Use your 'eyes' to look Inward for Inspiration – your Intuition, your Insight, your Intelligence, your Imagination, your Intention – and you will find the answers you seek.

THURSDAY **20**

Don't argue with reality

Relationships are like Rome – difficult to start out, incredible during the prosperity of the 'golden age', and unbearable during the fall. Then, a new kingdom will come along and the whole process will repeat itself until you come across a kingdom like Egypt... that thrives, and continues to flourish. This kingdom will become your best friend, your soul mate, and your love.

Helen Keller

FRIDAY **21**

Differentiate your desires from your hopes and wishes

SATURDAY **22**

Small talk may cause big disaster

SUNDAY **23**

Resist the urge to punish – it only leads to more suffering

Our lives improve only when we take chances; and the first and most difficult risk we can take is to be honest with ourselves.

Walter Anderson

Believe in yourself! Have faith in your abilities! Without a humble but reasonable confidence in your own powers you cannot be successful or happy.

Norman Vincent Peale

MONDAY **24**

We all have the capacity to be great

TUESDAY **25**

Embrace your humanity – we are all in the same boat

WEDNESDAY **26**

You are not alone

THURSDAY **27**

Cherish your ideals

August

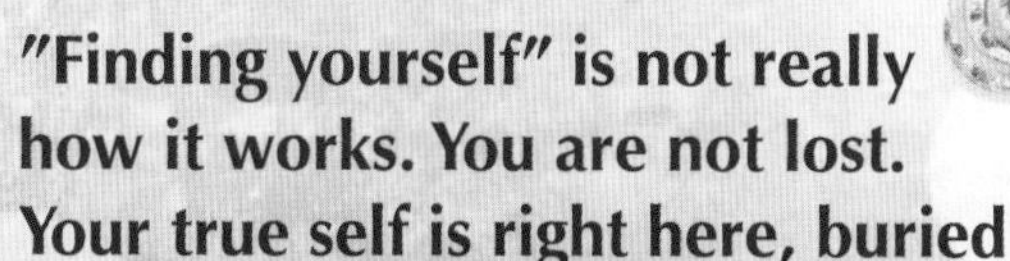

"Finding yourself" is not really how it works. You are not lost. Your true self is right here, buried under other people's opinions, and inaccurate conclusions you came to about yourself as a child, that became your beliefs about who you are. Finding yourself is actually returning to yourself, an unlearning, a discovery, a remembering who you were before the world put its words on you, and a re-creation of who you already know yourself to be.

FRIDAY **28**

Be the one you are looking for

SATURDAY **29**

Stay focussed at the task at hand

SUNDAY **30**

Be kind always

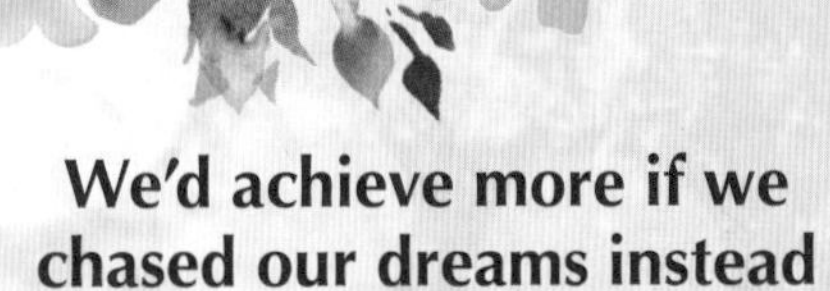

We'd achieve more if we chased our dreams instead of our competition.

Simon Sinek

MONDAY **31**

Acknowledge those who encouraged you

We do not need magic to change the world, we carry all the power we need inside ourselves already: we have the power to imagine better.

JK Rowling

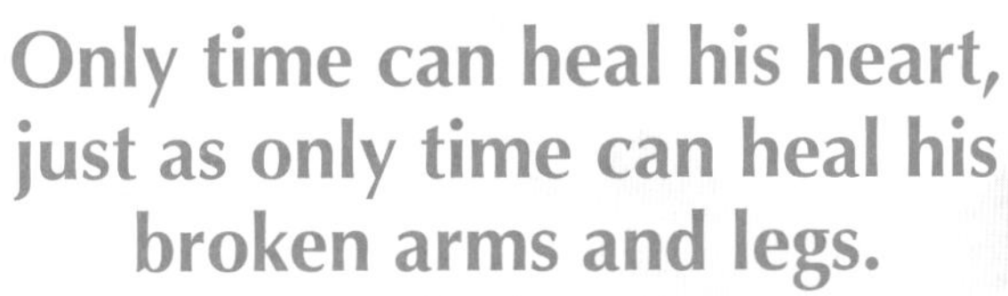

Miss Piggy

We are at our very best, and we are happiest, when we are fully engaged in work we enjoy on the journey toward the goal we've established for ourselves. It gives meaning to our time off and comfort to our sleep. It makes everything else in life so wonderful, so worthwhile.

Earl Nightingale

BUCKET LIST for September

Reflection MONTH

Welcome every morning with a smile. Look on the new day as another special gift from your creator. Another golden opportunity to complete what you were unable to finish yesterday. Let your first hour set the theme of success and positive action that is certain to echo through your entire day. Today will never happen again. Don't waste it with a false start or no start at all. You were not born to fail.

Og Mandino

TUESDAY **1**

You can find beauty everywhere – if you look for it

September

IF I COULD RAISE MY CHILDREN OVER AGAIN

If I had my child to raise all over again ..
I'd build self-esteem first, and the house later
I'd finger paint more, and point my finger less,
I'd do less correcting, and more connecting.
I'd take my eyes off my watch, and watch with my eyes
I would care to know less, and know to care more
I'd take more hikes and fly more kites
I'd stop playing serious, and seriously play
I would run through more fields and gaze at more stars
I'd do more hugging and less tugging
I'd see the oak tree and the acorn more often
I would be firm less often, and affirm much more.
I'd model less about the 'Love of Power'
And more about the 'Power of Love'.

Dianne Loomans

Crunchy choc slice

GLUTEN, DAIRY, AND REFINED SUGAR FREE – FROM MAMA RAE

WHAT YOU WILL NEED

200 gm buckwheat groats
½ cup cacao butter
½ cup coconut paste
1.4 cup goji berries

THE HOW-TO PART

Melt the cacao butter over low heat. Add the rest of the ingredients and mix. Pour into a flat dish 27×14 cm(10 ½x5 ½ in). Put into the refrigerator to set.

SECRETS FROM MAMA RAE'S KITCHEN

You can use any nuts instead of the buckwheat groats. Put them in a food processor and pulse until they are fine, but not to the point that they become a paste. If you don't have goji berries any other dried fruit works just as well. If you love chocolate add ½ cup of cacao or just make chocolate and pour over the top. Set in the refrigerator before cutting.

Maybe our girlfriends are our soulmates and guys are just people to have fun with.

Candace Bushnell

Don't let the fear of the time it will take to accomplish something stand in the way of your doing it. The time will pass anyway; we might just as well put that passing time to the best possible use.

Earl Nightingale

You learn so much from taking chances, whether they work out or not. Either way, you can grow from the experience and become stronger and smarter.

John Legend

WEDNESDAY **2**

Let those you love, know you love them

THURSDAY **3**

Nurture your friendships

How wrong it is for a woman to expect the man to build the world she wants, rather than to create it herself.

Anais Nin

No one can make you feel inferior without your consent.

Eleanor Roosevelt

September

It's one of the greatest gifts you can give yourself, to forgive. Forgive everybody.

Maya Angelou

Trust yourself. You know more than you think you do.

Benjamin Spock

You wouldn't worry so much about what others think of you if you realised how seldom they do.

Eleanor Roosevelt

FRIDAY **4**

Make excellence your goal, not perfection

SATURDAY **5**

Notice how you participate in life

SUNDAY **6**

Join a choir and sing out loud

You are, at this moment, standing, right in the middle of your own acres of diamonds.

Earl Nightingale

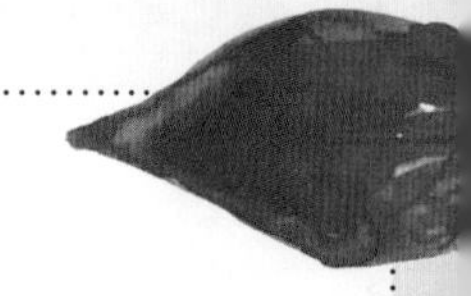

MONDAY **7**

Let your inner light shine through your smile

TUESDAY **8**

Don't worry about the future – just enjoy the present and plan

WEDNESDAY **9**

Take time to notice where you are

THURSDAY **10**

Help others to see the beauty in themselves

FRIDAY **11**

Be great enough to give and humble enough to receive

September

There are moments in life when you miss someone so much that you just want to pick them from your dreams and hug them for real!

When one door of happiness closes, another opens; but often we look so long at the closed door that we do not see the one that has been opened for us.

Helen Keller

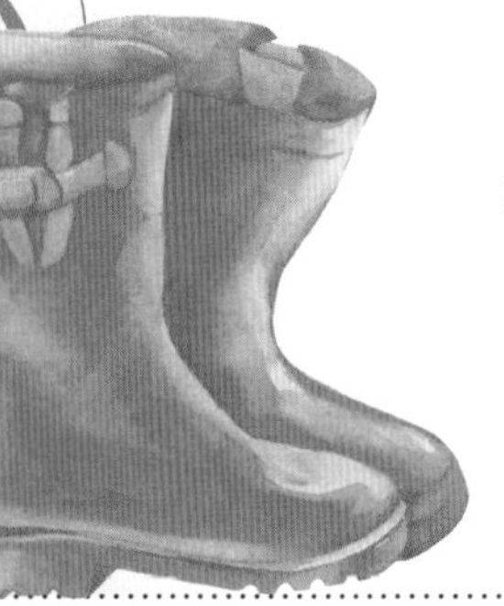

When the voice and vision on the inside, is more profound and clear and loud than all opinions on the outside, you have begun to master your life.

Dr John DImartini

SATURDAY **12**

Face the reality of the world with courage

SUNDAY **13**

Life's burdens are lightened by a quiet chuckle

Housework can't kill you, but why take a chance?

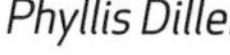

Phyllis Diller

MONDAY **14**

Nothing ventured, nothing gained

TUESDAY **15**

Don't hide behind a lie

Don't go for looks; they can deceive. Don't go for wealth; even that fades away. Go for someone who makes your heart smile, because it only takes a smile to make a dark day seem bright.

**Dream what you want to dream;
go where you want to go;
be what you want to be,
because you have only one life
and one chance to do all the things
you want to do.**

WEDNESDAY **16**

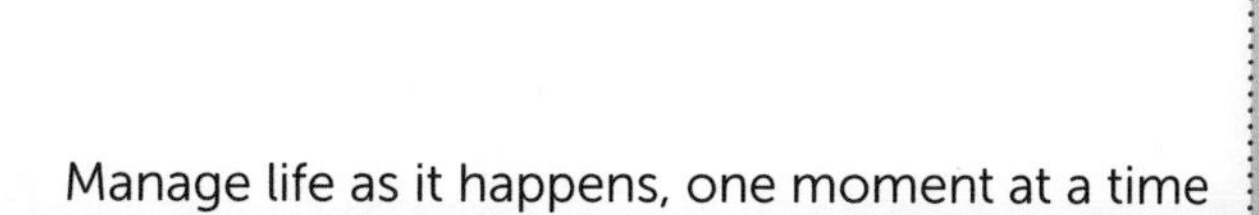

Manage life as it happens, one moment at a time

September

The big thing is that you know what you want.

Earl Nightingale

THURSDAY **17**

Dare to dream the possible

FRIDAY **18**

You are free to change your mind

SATURDAY **19**

Ask for support when you need it

SUNDAY **20**

Notice what you eat, and why

MONDAY **21**

Create an inspiring vision board

TUESDAY **22**

It takes a community to raise a person

WEDNESDAY **23**

Start with gratitude in your attitude

You can't connect the dots looking forward; you can only connect them looking backward. So you have to trust that the dots will somehow connect in your future. You have to trust in something; your gut, destiny, life, karma, whatever. This approach has never let me down, and it has made all the difference in my life.

Steve Jobs

The soul always knows what to do to heal itself. The challenge is to quieten the mind.

Caroline Myss

Our attitude towards others determines their attitude towards us.

Earl Nightingale

THURSDAY **24**

Who do you say that you are?

FRIDAY **25**

Start an autobiography 'Once upon a time a child was born.... '

SATURDAY **26**

Give yourself permission to laugh at yourself

SUNDAY **27**

Maybe you are perfect just as you are

I always did something I was a little not ready to do. I think that's how you grow. When there's that moment of 'Wow, I'm not really sure I can do this,' and you push through those moments, that's when you have a breakthrough.

Marissa Mayer

MONDAY **28**

'I can' and 'I will' is a way of life

TUESDAY **29**

Separate worries from concerns

WEDNESDAY **30**

Put your strengths to good use

Change your life today. Don't gamble on the future, act now, without delay.

Simone de Beauvoir

BUCKET LIST for October

Compassion MONTH

Owning our story can be hard but not nearly as difficult as spending our lives running from it.

Brené Brown

THURSDAY **1**

Don't make life your enemy

FRIDAY **2**

It's easier to go with the flow

MISS ME, BUT LET ME GO

When I come to the end of the road
And the sun has set for me
I want no rites in a gloom-filled room.
Why cry for a soul set free?

Miss me a little–but not too long
And not with your head bowed low.
Remember the love that we once shared,
Miss me–but let me go.

For this is a journey that we all must take
And each must go alone.
It's all a part of the Master's plan,
A step on the road to home.

When you are lonely and sick of heart
Go to the friends we know
And bury your sorrows in doing good deeds.
Miss Me, But Let me Go!

Christina Rossetti

SATURDAY **3**

Get rid of stuff you don't need

SUNDAY **4**

Early to bed and early to rise

October

Feel the Universe inside of you

SIMPLE RITUALS FOR SELF CARE

Schedule regular events *with family and friends*
Practice mindfulness. *Be present wherever you are. Experience every moment in its entirety – every occasion, location and conversation.*
Exercise. *It protects physical and emotional health, relieves stress, and makes you feel good. It's moving that matters.*
Spend some time outside. *Notice as colour and scenery changes around you – the lights, the smells, feel your feet on the ground. Sunlight is a great natural way to boost your mood.*
Deal with your emotions. *Learn how to properly deal with stress, anger, and anxiety instead of keeping them bottled up inside. Dialogue beats monologue every time!*
Be healthy inside. *Avoid junk food and stick to a healthy diet. Steer clear of smoking, drug use, and too much alcohol.*
Treat *your senses.* **Do little things** *like lighting a scented candle, buying some fresh-cut flowers, indulging in a massage or treating yourself to lunch with your favourite friend.*
Discover the benefits *of gentle Yoga The focus is on who you are 'being' rather than what you are 'doing'.*
Sleep. *Everyone gets cranky without enough sleep, so dedicate adequate sleep time every night.*
Keep a gratitude journal. *This provides you with time for reflection. Fill your gratitude journal with joyful encounters and special moments of connection, focusing on the happy bits. Perfection doesn't exist, but there is always something to be grateful for.*
Make happiness a priority. *Allow yourself to laugh and have fun. Let young people see that 'grown-ups' have a great life.*

We think sometimes that poverty is only being hungry, naked and homeless. The poverty of being unwanted, unloved and uncared for is the greatest poverty.

MONDAY **5**

Nothing will work unless you do

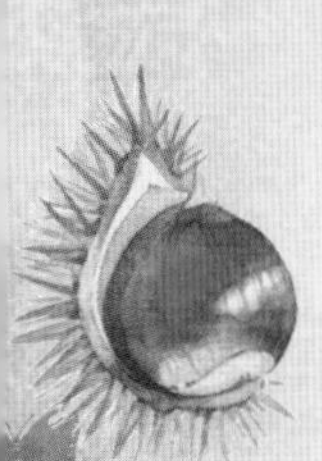

Every small positive change we make in ourselves repays us in confidence in the future.

Alice Walker

TUESDAY **6**

Put your energy into doing what you love

WEDNESDAY **7**

Value your own point of view – you've earned it

THURSDAY **8**

Go for a brisk walk and clear your head

FOR A HEALTHY MIND

Avoid envy.
Avoid regret.
Avoid resentments.
Avoid anxious fears.
Avoid anger.
Avoid inward fretting.
Avoid sadness not communicated.
Express hopes and dreams.
Express mirth.
Express delight.
Express wonder.
Express admiration.
Express gratitude.
Express love.

FRIDAY **9**

Relax, it's working out just fine

SATURDAY **10**

Let go of beliefs that no longer serve you

SUNDAY **11**

For each of us there are many turning points on our journey

MONDAY **12**

Remember there is no I in team player

When will our consciences grow so tender that we will act to prevent human misery rather than avenge it?

Mother Teresa

TUESDAY **13**

We are happiest when serving the greater good

WEDNESDAY **14**

Integrity is the foundation of all success

THURSDAY **15**

Surround yourself with people you admire

FRIDAY **16**

Choose the healthy option

Anzac biscuits

GLUTEN, DAIRY, AND REFINED SUGAR FREE – FROM MAMA RAE

WHAT YOU NEED

1 ½ cups quinoa flakes
¾ cup shredded coconut
¼ cup coconut oil
2-3 tablespoons maple syrup
1 teaspoon vanilla
½ teaspoon baking soda

THE HOW-TO PART

Turn your oven on to 150 degrees. Process 1 cup of the quinoa flakes, the shredded coconut, and the baking soda until it resembles breadcrumbs. Transfer to a bowl and add the rest of the quinoa flakes. Put all the wet ingredients into a separate bowl and mix before adding to the quinoa, coconut and soda. Stir until mixed evenly. You may want to add some water/milk, teaspoon by teaspoon so the mixture sticks together. Place teaspoonfuls of the mixture on a baking tray (line with baking paper if you wish) and then flatten with a fork. Bake your Anzac biscuits for 20 – 30 minutes, until they are golden brown.

SECRETS FROM MAMA RAE'S KITCHEN

You could use any other flakes, eg. oats or a mix of them. Try other oils instead of coconut. Macadamia oil is yummy but expensive. I have added ½ cup currants to this recipe or you could add ½ cup of slivered almonds for something different. They are a little bit fiddly to get into balls and flatten, but worth it. I sometimes use ginger syrup as the sweetener, for added flavour.

SATURDAY **17**

Sometimes it's ok just to be ok

SUNDAY **18**

Eat well balanced meals

Before you leave the house, you need to make up your mind that you're going to stay positive and enjoy the day no matter what comes your way. You have to decide ahead of time.

Joel Osteen

What I am looking for is not out there, it is in me.

Helen Keller

MONDAY **19**

Show up and step up, resist the temptation to give up

TUESDAY **20**

Be the leader in your own life

WEDNESDAY **21**

Visionary leaders are the saviours of the world

THURSDAY **22**

Push your luck

FRIDAY **23**

Love yourself anyway

October

I'm thankful for my struggle because without it I wouldn't have stumbled across my strength.

Alex Elle

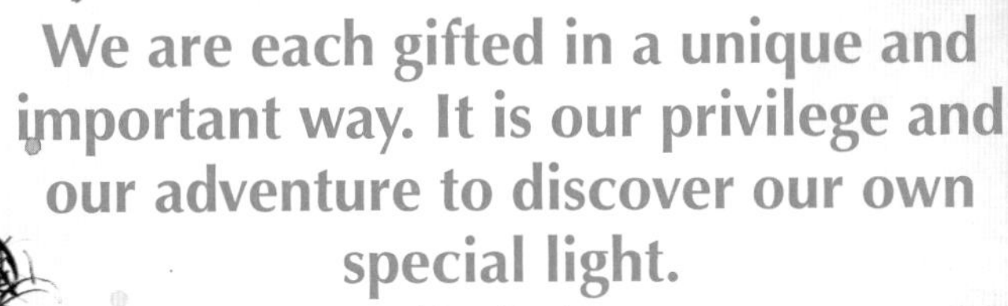

Mary Dunbar

I believe in being strong when everything seems to be going wrong. I believe that happy girls are the prettiest girls. I believe that tomorrow is another day and I believe in miracles.

Audrey Hepburn

SATURDAY **24**

Listen to music that comforts you

SUNDAY **25**

Love makes all things possible

MONDAY **26**
Bank holiday

Live out loud

TUESDAY **27**

Do not fret over old griefs

WEDNESDAY **28**

Understand that life is not fair

THURSDAY **29**

Be open to new suggestions

The truest greatness lies in being kind, the truest wisdom in a happy mind.

Ella Wheeler Wilcox

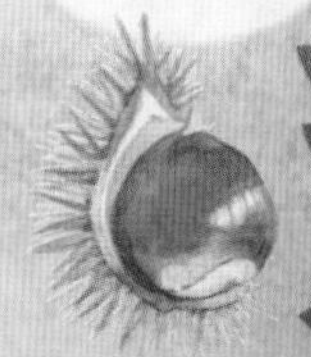

I am determined to be cheerful and happy in whatever situation I may find myself. For I have learned that the greater part of our misery or unhappiness is determined not by our circumstance but by our disposition.

Martha Washington

FRIDAY **30**

Stop trying to do it all

SATURDAY **31**

A bath can be a mini-vacation

One's life has value so long as one attributes value to the life of others, by means of love, friendship, indignation and compassion.

Simone de Beauvoir

Learn to enjoy every minute of your life. Be happy now. Don't wait for something outside of yourself to make you happy in the future. Think how really precious is the time you have to spend, whether it's at work or with your family. Every minute should be enjoyed and savoured.

Earl Nightingale

BUCKET LIST for *November*

Wisdom MONTH

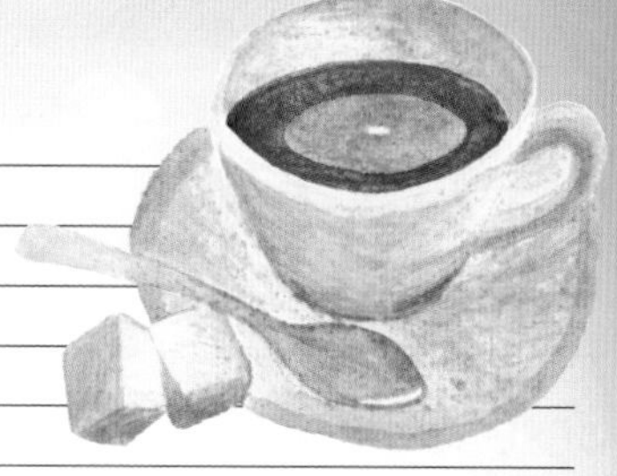

Realise that true happiness lies within you. Waste no time and effort searching for peace and contentment and joy in the world outside. Remember that there is no happiness in having or in getting, but only in giving. Reach out. Share. Smile. Hug. Happiness is a perfume you cannot pour on others without getting a few drops on yourself.

Og Mandino

SUNDAY **1**

Write down your goals

November

Love is the great miracle cure. Loving ourselves works miracles in our lives.

Louise Hay

MONDAY **2**

Panic can be used for energy

TUESDAY **3**

Forgive others for their mistakes and move on

WEDNESDAY **4**

Don't gossip

THURSDAY **5**

Life is messy despite how it appears on the small screen

If we listened to our intellect,
we'd never have a love affair.
We'd never have a friendship.
We'd never go into business
because we'd be too cynical.
Well, that's nonsense.
You've got to jump off cliffs
all the time and
build your wings on
the way down.

Annie Dillard

FRIDAY **6**

Everyone lays a burden on the willing horse

SATURDAY **7**

Express your concerns to an impartial listener

SUNDAY **8**

Find love within yourself

November

When the root is deep, there's no fear of the wind.

MONDAY **9**

Enhance the confidence of others

TUESDAY **10**

What pains us trains us

WEDNESDAY **11**

Don't waste precious energy (and time) on what you can't control

THURSDAY **12**

Focus on the positive

I forgive myself and I set myself free.
Louise Hay

FRIDAY **13**

When things go wrong, don't go wrong with them

Remember that children, marriages, and flower gardens reflect the kind of care they get.

H Jackson Brown Jr

Courgette pizza

GLUTEN AND DAIRY FREE – FROM MAMA RAE

WHAT YOU WILL NEED

Base
6 medium courgettes
½ cup nutritional yeast
2 crushed cloves garlic
1 tablespoon oregano
2/3 cups gluten free flour
1 egg
Salt and pepper

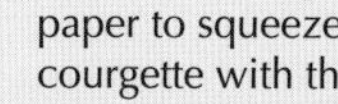

THE HOW-TO PART

Grate the courgette and steam for a few minutes. Then use kitchen paper to squeeze as much of the water out as possible. Mix the courgette with the rest of the ingredients. Place a piece of baking paper in a tray and form the dough into 2 x 18 cm pizzas. Bake at 190 degrees for 15 – 20 minutes until the edges are brown.
Add any of these toppings – tomato paste/pesto/watercress/capsicum/olives or artichokes, or any of your own choice. Bake for another 15 minutes

SECRETS FROM MAMA RAE'S KITCHEN

For the pesto: process 1 bunch of basil, I bunch parsley 1 bunch coriander and a packet of chives with 1 cup of olive oil and 1 teaspoon herb salt. Vary the herbs. I use 2 bunches of coriander.
I like to use chickpea/besan flour as the gluten free flour. You can replace the egg with 1 tablespoon of chia seeds (soak for 15 minutes in 3 tablespoons water). You can make into smaller pizzas.

SATURDAY **14**

What the eyes see can change what the mind believes

SUNDAY **15**

Beauty comes from the soul

November

And the day came when the risk to remain tight in a bud was more painful than the risk it took to blossom.

Anais Nin

MONDAY **16**

Review your life regularly

TUESDAY **17**

Foresight is better than hindsight – but insight beats both

WEDNESDAY **18**

Take time out to tune in to where you are

A lifetime isn't forever, so take the first chance, don't wait for the second one! Because sometimes, there aren't second chances! And if it turns out to be a mistake? So what! This is life! A whole bunch of mistakes!

C JoyBell

No matter how difficult and painful it may be, nothing sounds as good to the soul as the truth.

Martha Beck

THURSDAY **19**

It's a noisy world

FRIDAY **20**

Be the hero of your own story

SATURDAY **21**

Make peace with your past

SUNDAY **22**

Don't be offended by the truth

I learned compassion from being discriminated against. Everything bad that's ever happened to me has taught me compassion.

Ellen DeGeneres

November

Many receive advice, only the wise profit from it.

Harper Lee

MONDAY **23**

You have all the love you need inside yourself

TUESDAY **24**

Pamper yourself now and again

WEDNESDAY **25**

Don't live life so you die disappointed

All of us are beset by fears and pain and doubts. We let ourselves get turned away from our goals by obstructions. But it is possible, as Marie Curie once reminded us, to change our world so that nothing in life is to be feared, only understood.

Og Mandino

If you want to understand your parents more, get them to talk about their own childhood; and if you listen with compassion, you will learn where their fears and rigid patterns come from. Those people who "did all that stuff to you" were just as frightened and scared as you are.

Louise Hay

THURSDAY **26**

What you don't ask for you don't get

FRIDAY **27**

Search for the truth in others' opinions

SATURDAY **28**

Avoid making too many changes at once

SUNDAY **29**

Conduct yourself with dignity

Keep your words soft and sweet, in case you have to eat them!

November

IF I HAD MY LIFE OVER

(in memory of a mother who lost her fight with cancer)

I would have talked less and listened more.
I would have invited friends over to dinner,
even if the carpet was stained and the sofa faded.
I would have eaten the popcorn in the good living room and worried
less about the dirt when someone wanted to light a fire in the fireplace.
I would have taken the time to listen to my grandfather
ramble on about his youth.
I would never insist that the car windows be rolled up on a
summer's day because my hair had just been done.
I would have burned the pink candle, sculpted like a rose,
before it melted in storage.
I would have sat on the lawn with my children
and not worried about grass stains.
I would have cried and laughed less while
watching television, and more while watching life.
I would have shared more of the responsibility carried by my husband.
I would have gone to bed when I was sick instead of pretending that the
world would go into a holding pattern if I weren't there for a day.
I would never have bought anything just because it was practical,
wouldn't show soil, or was guaranteed to last a lifetime.
Instead of wishing away nine months of pregnancy,
I'd have cherished every moment and realised that it
was the only chance I had in assisting God with a miracle.
When my kids wanted to kiss me impetuously,
I would never have said, 'Later, now go wash up for dinner"
There would have been more "I love you's" and more "I'm sorry's"
Given another shot at life, I would seize every minute ... look at it,
... hold it ... and never give it back.

Irma Bombeck

MONDAY **30**

Respect the concerns of others

CHRISTMAS SHOPPING LIST

1. Buy a 2021 Get Up and Go Diary for all my friends.
2. Buy a Get Up and Go Travel Journal and plan my next trip.
3. Buy a Daily Planner for...
4. Buy a Genius Journal for...

BUCKET LIST
for
December
Peace MONTH
There is no way to peace.
Peace is the way.
Never will I allow myself to become
so important, so wise, so dignified,
so powerful, that I forget how to
laugh at myself and my world.
Og Mandino

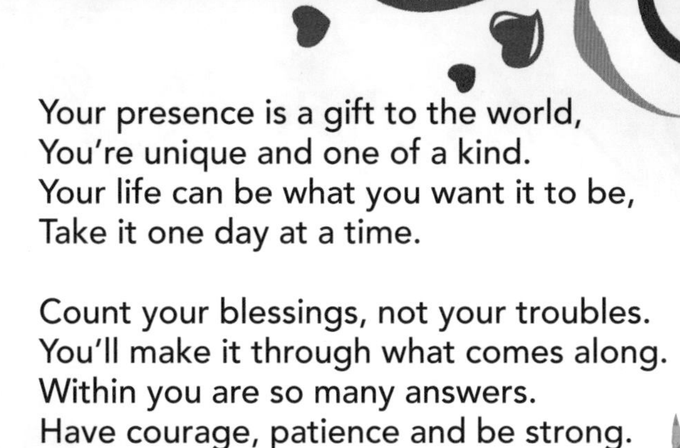

Your presence is a gift to the world,
You're unique and one of a kind.
Your life can be what you want it to be,
Take it one day at a time.

Count your blessings, not your troubles.
You'll make it through what comes along.
Within you are so many answers.
Have courage, patience and be strong.

Don't put limits on yourself,
Your dreams deserve to be realised.
Don't leave your important decisions to chance.
Reach for your goal, your peak, your prize.

Nothing wastes more time than worrying,
Hiding the problem ensures the heavier it gets.
Don't take matters too seriously,
Live a life of serenity, not one of regrets.

Remember, a little love goes a long way,
Remember that a lot goes forever,
Remember that friendship is a wise investment,
Life's treasures are people ... together.

Have health and hope and happiness.
Take the time to wish on a star.
And don't forget, for even a day,
How very special you are.

TUESDAY **1**

Tune in to what makes your heart sing

December

People are like stained glass windows. They sparkle and shine when the sun is out, but when the darkness sets in, their true beauty is revealed only if there is a light from within.

Elisabeth Kubler-Ross

I long to accomplish a great and noble task, but it is my chief duty to accomplish small tasks as if they were great and noble. The world is moved along, not only by the mighty shoves of its heroes, but also the aggregate of the tiny pushes of each honest worker.

Helen Keller

A mother is a person who seeing there are only four pieces of pie for five people, promptly announces she never did care for pie.

Tenneva Jordan

WEDNESDAY **2**

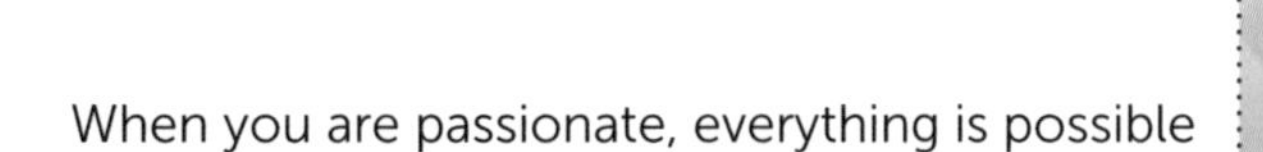

When you are passionate, everything is possible

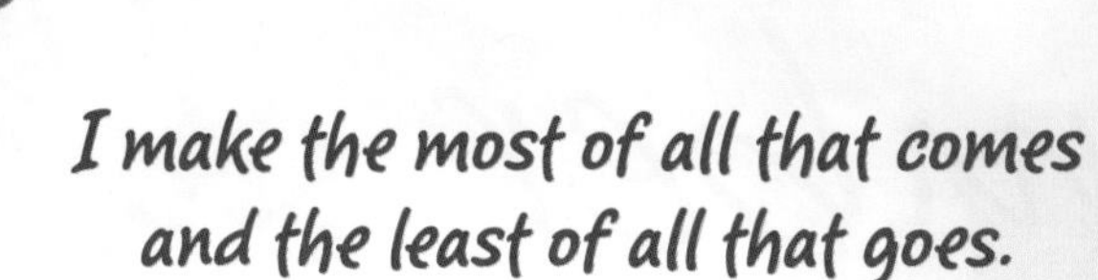

Sara Teasdale

THURSDAY **3**

Be a willing explorer in your life

FRIDAY **4**

There is no way that people, or the world, should be

SATURDAY **5**

What we think is what we think

SUNDAY **6**

Get to know your neighbours

That last page turned is a perfect excuse to write a whole new book.

Toni Sorenson

December

There is nothing more rare, nor more beautiful, than a woman being unapologetically herself; comfortable in her perfect imperfection. To me, that is the true essence of beauty.

Steve Maraboli

You are unique, and if that is not fulfilled then something has been lost.

Martha Graham

Anger is the ultimate destroyer of peace of mind. We can never obtain peace in the outer world until we make peace with ourselves.

Dalai Lama

Pomegranate cosmo

MAKES 4

INGREDIENTS

$^{2}/_{3}$ cup of pomegranate juice
$^{1}/_{2}$ cup of vodka
$^{1}/_{4}$ cup of Grand Marnier or Cointreau
2 teaspoons of fresh lime juice
Ice
Lime slices

DIRECTIONS

1. Mix everything except the lime slices together.
2. Strain into a glass.
3. Garnish with a lime slice.

MONDAY **7**

The only failing in life is not trying

If you want peace of mind, stop fighting with your thoughts.

TUESDAY **8**

Stay connected with what lights you up

Leadership is about making others better as a result of your presence and making sure that impact lasts in your absence.

Sheryl Sandberg

You are the one that possesses the keys to your being. You carry the passport to your own happiness. Don't put the keys to your happiness in someone else's pocket.

WEDNESDAY **9**

Thank the 'voice in your ear' for sharing and move on

THURSDAY **10**

Ditch the 'cudda, wudda, shudda' sisters

December

Make the most of yourself by fanning the tiny, inner sparks of possibility into flames of achievement.

Golda Meir

Take criticism seriously, but not personally. If there is truth or merit in the criticism, try to learn from it. Otherwise, let it roll right off you.

Hillary Clinton

FRIDAY **11**

Rise and shine every morning – like the sun

SATURDAY **12**

Don't wait for a health crisis to remind you how precious life is

SUNDAY **13**

Schedule at least four getaway breaks per year

So long as the memory of certain beloved friends lives in my heart, I shall say that life is good.

Helen Keller

MONDAY **14**

Listen to your body

Hold your head and your standards high even as people, or circumstances, try to pull you down.

Tory Johnson

TUESDAY **15**

This is your life

WEDNESDAY **16**

Don't blame others for your upset

THURSDAY **17**

Stop making excuses

December

My heart forgives and releases. Inner peace is my goal.

Louise Hay

FRIDAY **18**

Be a compassionate human being

I do not try to dance better than anyone else. I only try to dance better than myself.

Arianna Huffington

If you can't go straight ahead, you go around the corner.

Cher

SATURDAY **19**

Take time to heal the suffering of the past

SUNDAY **20**

What we say makes a difference

The best thing to hold onto in life is each other.

Audrey Hepburn

MONDAY **21**

Stop chasing perfect

There are two kinds of people, those who do the work and those who take the credit. Try to be in the first group; there is less competition there.

Indira Gandhi

When you embrace your difference, your DNA, your look or heritage or religion or your unusual name, that's when you start to shine.

Betheny Frankel

The life of inner peace, being harmonious and without stress, is the easiest type of existence.

Norman Vincent Peale

Roast lemon leeks

GLUTEN AND DAIRY FREE – FROM MAMA RAE

WHAT YOU WILL NEED

4 large leeks
2 tablespoons oil
Juice and zest of 1 lemon
¼ cup water
Black pepper

THE HOW-TO PART

Turn the oven on to 170 degrees C. Wash the leeks well. Slice the leeks into 7 ½ cm pieces and put into a dish. Add the lemon zest and juice, the oil and the water. Sprinkle with black pepper.
Put into oven and bake for 25-30 minutes.

SECRETS FROM MAMA RAE'S KITCHEN

If you are cooking for two the you would only need 1, maybe 1 ½ leeks.

The challenge is not to be perfect...it's to be whole.

Jane Fonda

December

TUESDAY **22**

You are worthy of a great life

Normal is not something to aspire to, it's something to get away from.

Jodie Foster

When I'm hungry, I eat. When I'm thirsty, I drink. When I feel like saying something, I say it.

Madonna

Everyone shines, given the right lighting.

Susan Cain

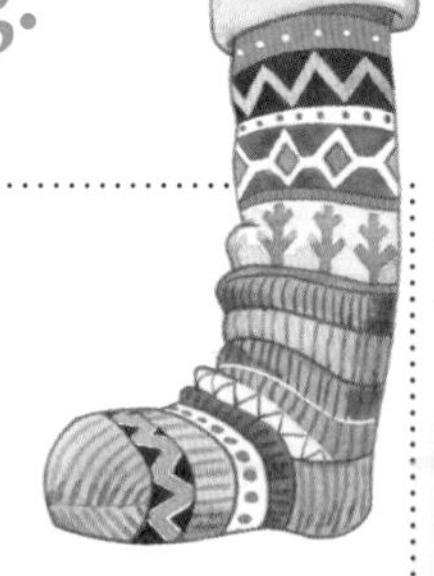

WEDNESDAY **23**

Beware the enemy within

THURSDAY **24**

Give simple gifts

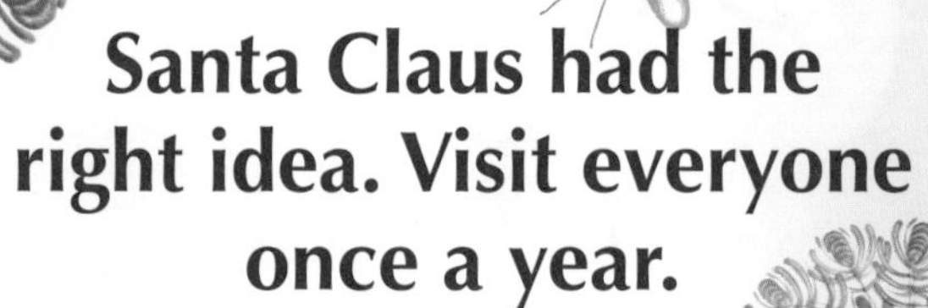

Santa Claus had the right idea. Visit everyone once a year.

Victor Borges.

Whenever you are blue or lonely or stricken by some humiliating thing you did, the cure and the hope is in caring about other people.

Diane Sawyer

I try to live in a little bit of my own joy and not let people steal it or take it.

FRIDAY **25**
Christmas Day

Those who love you know who you are, and love you anyway!

SATURDAY **26**

The proof is in the pudding

SUNDAY **27**

Try out new conversations with new people

MONDAY **28**

We don't need an explanation for everything

TUESDAY **29**

It takes courage to stand for yourself

WEDNESDAY **30**

It is ok to ask for what you want

Style is a way to say who you are without having to speak.

Rachel Zoe

THURSDAY **31**
New Year's Eve

How big is your vision

An optimist stays up until midnight to see the New Year in. A pessimist stays up to make sure the old year leaves.

Bill Vaughn

This journey has always been about reaching your own other shore no matter what it is, and that dream continues.

Diana Nyad

When you're through changing, you're through.

Martha Stewart

It's not the absence of fear, it's overcoming it. Sometimes you've got to blast through and have faith.

Emma Watson

And in the end, it's not the years in your life that count, it's the life in your years.

Abraham Lincoln

DESIDERATA

Go placidly amid the noise and haste, and remember what peace there may be in silence. As far as possible without surrender be on good terms with all persons. Speak your truth quietly and clearly, and listen to others, even the dull and ignorant; they too have their story.

Avoid loud and aggressive persons, they are vexations to the spirit. If you compare yourself with others, you may become vain and bitter; for always there will be greater and lesser persons than yourself. Enjoy your achievements as well as your plans. Keep interested in your own career, however humble; it is a real possession in the changing fortunes of time. Exercise caution in your business affairs; for the world is full of trickery. But let this not blind you to what virtue there is; many persons strive for high ideals; and everywhere life is full of heroism.

Be yourself. Especially, do not feign affection. Neither be cynical about love; for in the face of all aridity and disenchantment it is perennial as the grass. Take kindly the counsel of the years, gracefully surrendering the things of youth. Nurture strength of spirit to shield you in sudden misfortune. But do not distress yourself with imaginings. Many fears are born of fatigue and loneliness. Beyond a wholesome discipline, be gentle with yourself.

You are a child of the universe, no less than the trees and the stars; you have a right to be here. And whether or not it is clear to you, no doubt the universe is unfolding as it should. Therefore be at peace with God, whatever you conceive Him to be; and whatever your labours and aspirations, in the noisy confusion of life keep peace with your soul. With all its sham, drudgery and broken dreams, it is still a beautiful world. Be cheerful. Strive to be happy.

Max Ehrmann

2021 CALENDAR

January

S	M	T	W	T	F	S
					1	2
3	4	5	6	7	8	9
10	11	12	13	14	15	16
17	18	19	20	21	22	23
24	25	26	27	28	29	30
31						

February

S	M	T	W	T	F	S
	1	2	3	4	5	6
7	8	9	10	11	12	13
14	15	16	17	18	19	20
21	22	23	24	25	26	27
28						

March

S	M	T	W	T	F	S
	1	2	3	4	5	6
7	8	9	10	11	12	13
14	15	16	17	18	19	20
21	22	23	24	25	26	27
28	29	30	31			

April

S	M	T	W	T	F	S
				1	2	3
4	5	6	7	8	9	10
11	12	13	14	15	16	17
18	19	20	21	22	23	24
25	26	27	28	29	30	

May

S	M	T	W	T	F	S
						1
2	3	4	5	6	7	8
9	10	11	12	13	14	15
16	17	18	19	20	21	22
23	24	25	26	27	28	29
30	31					

June

S	M	T	W	T	F	S
		1	2	3	4	5
6	7	8	9	10	11	12
13	14	15	16	17	18	19
20	21	22	23	24	25	26
27	28	29	30			

July

S	M	T	W	T	F	S
				1	2	3
4	5	6	7	8	9	10
11	12	13	14	15	16	17
18	19	20	21	22	23	24
25	26	27	28	29	30	31

August

S	M	T	W	T	F	S
1	2	3	4	5	6	7
8	9	10	11	12	13	14
15	16	17	18	19	20	21
22	23	24	25	26	27	28
29	30	31				

September

S	M	T	W	T	F	S
			1	2	3	4
5	6	7	8	9	10	11
12	13	14	15	16	17	18
19	20	21	22	23	24	25
26	27	28	29	30		

October

S	M	T	W	T	F	S
					1	2
3	4	5	6	7	8	9
10	11	12	13	14	15	16
17	18	19	20	21	22	23
24	25	26	27	28	29	30
31						

November

S	M	T	W	T	F	S
	1	2	3	4	5	6
7	8	9	10	11	12	13
14	15	16	17	18	19	20
21	22	23	24	25	26	27
28	29	30				

December

S	M	T	W	T	F	S
			1	2	3	4
5	6	7	8	9	10	11
12	13	14	15	16	17	18
19	20	21	22	23	24	25
26	27	28	29	30	31	

FOR MORE COPIES VISIT OUR WEBSITE

www.getupandgodiary.com

OR CONTACT US ON

info@getupandgodiary.com

Postal address: **Get Up and Go Publications Ltd, Camboline, Hazelwood, Sligo, Ireland F91 NP04**.

For current prices, special offers and postal charges for your region, please refer to the website (www.getupandgodiary.com).

DIRECT ORDER FORM (please complete by ticking boxes)

PLEASE SEND ME:

The Irish Get Up and Go Diary	Year		Quantity	
The Irish Get Up and Go Diary (case bound)	Year		Quantity	
Get Up and Go Diary for Busy Women	Year		Quantity	
Get Up and Go Diary for Busy Women (case bound)	Year		Quantity	
Get Up and Go Diary	Year		Quantity	
Get Up and Go Young Persons' Diary	Year		Quantity	
Get Up and Go All Stars Sports Journal	Year		Quantity	
Get Up and Go Daily Planner for Busy Women	Year		Quantity	
Get Up and Go Gratitude Journal			Quantity	
Get Up and Go Wallplanner	Year		Quantity	
Get Up and Go Travel Journal			Quantity	
Get Up and Go Genius Journal			Quantity	
Get Up and Go Student Journal (homework journal)	Year		Quantity	
Get Up and Go Heroes (all proceeds to charity)			Quantity	
The Confidence to Succeed (by Donna Kennedy)			Quantity	
			Total number of copies	

I enclose cheque/postal order for (total amount including P+P): ____________________

Name: ____________________

Address: ____________________

Contact phone number: ____________ Email: ____________________

For queries, please contact us on 071 9146717/085 1764297.